WILLIAM

THE MAN WHO NEVER GAVE UP

BOOKS IN THE SAME SERIES:

Prisoner from Beyond the River by Geoffrey Bull

William and Catherine Booth: God's Soldiers by Jenty Fairbanks

The Secret Country: A children's life of C. S. Lewis by Anne Arnott

WILLIAM CAREY

The Man who Never Gave Up

NANCY MARTIN

HODDER AND STOUGHTON
LONDON SYDNEY AUCKLAND TORONTO

 ISBN 0 340 18096 X. *Printed in Great Britain for Hodder and Stoughton Limited, St. Paul's House, Warwick Lane, LONDON EC4P 4AH by Cox & Wyman Ltd, London, Reading and Fakenham*

Contents

I

William's New Home

It was moving day for the Careys. Young William, the eldest of the children, was six. From the little cottage in the hollow at Pury End, where he was born, William could see the house where he was to live. It was set on a hill close by the church, its garden divided from the rectory grounds by a moat full of water.

There were a lot of things William liked about his new home. In the moat he would be able to fish for sticklebacks and tadpoles and even more interesting things. At the back of the house there was a garden with an orchard, and in the front, two big plane trees, all good places for climbing.

The school, a low-thatched building, adjoined the house and in front of the school there was a small playground. No desks were provided, only rough tree slabs for benches. William's father was to be the schoolmaster, which meant that William would be one of the lucky boys who would have a place there. His grandfather had been the first master of Pury School, which was built when village schools were few in number, with only a few free places. National schools had not even been heard of.

Best of all, the schoolhouse, though small, was bigger

than the cottage they had been living in and now William was given a room of his own where he could keep his treasures.

Paulerspury was a quiet, unspoilt village, eleven miles south of Northampton, near Towcester. The royal forest of Whittlebury bordered the village and only a few hundred yards away stage coaches could be seen making their long, slow journey to and from London. In those days it took twenty hours to travel from Leicester to London. Today it takes an hour and a half by fast train, or about two hours by road.

The move from Pury End to Paulerspury took place in 1767. It was the first of many important events which were to change not only William's life but the lives of millions of people throughout the world. This small determined boy, living in an obscure village in Northamptonshire, in the centre of England, was to become the man who was to spend his life in the service of others, giving the Gospel to the peoples of India. He was to be the first to translate the Bible into most of the main Indian languages.

Yet he was of humble origin. His father was a cottage-weaver before becoming schoolmaster, and much respected in the village. His mother was a lace-maker. It was a happy household, though poor, with seven people to be fed on a small income. Edmund and Elizabeth Carey were a deeply religious couple, strictly observing Sunday, regularly attending the parish church with their family, as was the custom, so that William early became familiar with the prayer book. He was encouraged to read the Bible and to memorise many passages, though he disliked reading religious books.

Great changes were taking place in the industrial life of

England, but the industrial revolution had not yet started. When William was only four years of age James Watt invented the steam engine and two years later Hargreaves' spinning-jenny was invented. In the same year new avenues of travel were being opened up by Brindley's engineering of canals.

The Wesley brothers, and Whitefield, in speech and song, were rousing people to a new understanding of God's love for men with their evangelising message.

Streets in the towns were beginning to be lit by oil lamps, but village homes were lit with rushlights. These were tiny bowls of fat or tallow with rush wicks.

In the wider world Captain Cook was planning his first voyage to new lands. A group of English merchants had banded themselves together to form the East India Company, which had been settled in India as a political power for many years. Robert Clive had laid the foundations of a British dominated state in the province of Bengal. About the time Carey was born Clive had returned to England and been given high honours before being reappointed as Governor of Bengal. England, in common with other countries, was heavily engaged in the slave trade. The hostility towards, and exploitation of the coloured populations of the world was deplorable. They were only wanted as cheap labour. There were thousands of negro slaves in London and newspapers advertised children for sale with rewards offered for runaways.

British people were not entirely free; men were seized by the press gang without warning and forced to join ships of war, or impressed into the service of the East India Company or the American Colonies.

These events hardly touched the village where the

Careys lived, though they were not unaware of them. Paulerspury, with its cottage industries and handicrafts, its pastures and cornfields, was almost self-contained, and William passed his earliest years in an atmosphere of peace and contentment. In the summer the children helped with haymaking and rode on the haycarts drawn by horses with jingling bells. When the harvest was gathered everyone joined in the rejoicing at the harvest supper in the great barns. On the village green, close by the church, they played their games, William being as keen and enthusiastic as any. Occasionally the pedlar arrived with his wares, or there was a country fair to which the village children were driven in farm wagons decorated with ribbons and branches of trees.

In his new home in the schoolhouse, William's days were fully occupied. Soon he had his room filled with birds and insects of all kinds. Every morning he was up early, cleaning out his bird-cages and his pets' houses. He gathered food for them from the lanes and hedgerows. His mother sent him to get firewood from the forest and water from the spring down the lane and as he went he noticed the changes in nature and delighted in the wild life all around. When he reached home he made careful notes of what he had seen.

Sometimes he took with him his younger brother Tom, carrying him most of the way, showing him the beauties of individual flowers and plants and describing birds, insects and butterflies. Mary was his favourite and most understanding sister. Together they listened to the nightingales singing in Whittlebury woods. She followed him everywhere, crossing the dirtiest roads to get a particular plant or insect and learning from him all the time. When her brother was away from home, she was left in charge of his birds and insects. Often she killed them by kindness, but when he saw how this upset her he forgave her and let her go on caring for them.

Though only a small boy, shorter than many boys of his age, he had plenty of courage, energy and initiative. Nothing daunted him. Once, when he had a tooth he wanted taken out, he tied a piece of string to the tooth and fixed it to a grindwheel. Then he got a boy to give a turn to the wheel and the tooth was out. He could climb the most difficult trees to find a bird's nest and when he lost his footing and fell to the ground he was soon climbing the same tree again. When his mother complained about this he said:

'I couldn't help it, mother. I couldn't really. If I begin a thing I must go through with it.'

This was an attitude which characterised all he did right through his life. It was this persistence which eventually took him to his life's work in India.

As a boy of six he showed signs of having a good mathematical brain. He was often heard counting when he should have been asleep. His father was a good teacher but did not praise his own children for their talents, in fact he was inclined to belittle them. Reading, writing and arithmetic were the main subjects he taught. William very quickly learned to draw sufficiently well to help him in his research in natural history. He had an attentive and receptive mind, coupled with an industrious nature. Years later, when writing from India to his nephew, he said:

'I can plod. That is my only genius. I can persevere in any definite pursuit. To this I owe everything.'

He was certainly a plodder, but he was over modest in

saying it was his only genius. Before he left school he had shown an ability to master languages; so much so that when he was twelve years old he memorised sixty pages of a Latin Vocabulary.

Of the many people who influenced him in his early years, his uncle Peter probably played as great a part as any. After living for some years in Canada he returned to England and settled as head gardener on a big estate in Paulerspury. He told his young nephew stories about his travels and his meeting with the Indians and the French in different parts of Canada. He told him stories of the sea and ships and about the lakes, rivers and falls in Canada. He shared William's interest in natural history and gave him a love of gardening. Quite early in life William took charge of his father's garden and soon it became the best in the village. In fact, he became so knowledgeable on these things that when anyone had a flower or insect he could not recognise he would be told:

'Take it to Bill Carey. He'll tell you all about it.'

Uncle Peter brought the great wide world to William and found him an eager listener. All this was making a tremendous impression on the boy. The more he listened the wider his interests became. Perhaps it was Uncle Peter who told him about Columbus and the discovery of America. At any rate, it so fired his imagination that he was always talking about the great explorer and his school fellows nicknamed him Columbus.

By the time William was ten years old Captain Cook had returned from his first voyage to the South Seas, giving the boy more food for thought and a still greater interest in other countries. Possibly the fact that Cook was the son of a Yorkshire labourer and had gone into the Navy as a common seaman, made William believe in his own ability to make his contribution in some way.

And then there were the books. He chose to read books on science, history and travel; he had little interest in fiction, though Defoe's stories of Robinson Crusoe probably made a greater impact on his future than he realised.

Religion and church-going at that time meant little to him, though he was in the choir at the village church for a brief period. The choir boys were rough and uncouth and caused him to lose the little interest he had in religion. In fact, as a boy, William Carey was neither particularly bad nor religious. He was just an ordinary boy with a boy's zest for living, though he said he was in the habit of lying and swearing.

2

Growing Up

IT IS NOT SURPRISING THAT WHEN WILLIAM LEFT SCHOOL at fourteen years of age he wanted to work on the land like his uncle. For two years he was happily employed in this way. He would doubtless have continued in this work for quite a while but for a skin irritation thought to be caused by his being so much exposed to the sun. For two years he fought against it, loving his work and not being the type to give in easily. But when it became so painful that he could not sleep at night he was forced to accept defeat.

Pearce Carey, when writing his biography of his great-grandfather, remarks on the fact that he who was 'to endure forty years of Bengal heat was turned from his chosen path by distress of English sunshine'.

Though William was unaware of it at the time, and probably rebelled against being forced to take a different job, this was yet another landmark in his life. He left home to live at the premises of the shoemaker for whom he was to work.

When Edmund Carey apprenticed his son to Clarke Nichols, the shoemaker at Piddington, some nine miles from Paulerspury, there was nothing to indicate that the boy's life would be completely changed as a result. Shoemaking was becoming the chief craft of Northampton and doubtless Edmund Carey considered this would provide his eldest son with a sound trade for the future. Clarke Nichols was reputed to be a strict churchman, but his quick temper and Saturday-night drinking bouts were no recommendation for his religion. Also, the fact that he was a church-goer did not prevent him from sending his young apprentice, on Sunday mornings, delivering the week's supply of boots and shoes which had been made or mended.

In spite of the influence of his home and his regular attendance at church, William had not become a committed Christian. Now, away from home influence, and with such a poor example in his employer, he soon tired of religious practices. Doubtless too, he was not finding shoemaking and mending much to his liking after his two years of work in the garden. He made friends with those who had no interest in church attendance, and were in the habit of lying and swearing. But for the influence of his fellow apprentice, John Warr, who was three years older, Carey's story might have been entirely different.

John Warr was pleased to have William working with him and sharing the attic bedroom. He had come from Potterspury, the twin village to Paulerspury, and had already acquired a good knowledge of the shoe trade because his father and his grandfather had been engaged in it all their lives. John shared his knowledge with his fellow apprentice, showing him how to prepare the leather, to use the tools, to cut the welts and uppers, as well as the soles and heels.

Not only had John Warr's grandfather been a

shoemaker, but he had been partly responsible for the founding of the Independent Church in Potterspury. Although John had not yet consciously committed himself to Christ, he was seeking his way. He talked a lot about this to William as they worked at the bench, trying to make him understand why so many people had left the Anglican church and were forming their own independent churches. But though Carey was moving away from church, he argued strongly against the dissenters, whose children had not been allowed to go to the Pury school where his father taught.

Possibly Carey's intolerance only made John seek the harder to find the truth, for soon he consciously accepted Christ as his Saviour and then he wanted William to do the same. There were plenty of books in the home at Potterspury and John urged his friend to read them. In spite of himself William was impressed and gradually he became aware of the fact that he needed a change of heart.

At this time something happened which caused him to feel a tremendous sense of guilt. It was the season of Christmas, and one of the shoemaker's customers offered William the choice of a shilling or a sixpence as a Christmas box. As was to be expected, the lad chose the shilling, but when he wanted to spend it he discovered it was a bad one.

Writing about the incident later, he described the way he wrestled with his conscience about the matter:

> I was strongly inclined to assert to my master that it belonged to other money with which he had entrusted me to purchase things for him, as this could clear my private account. I recollect the struggle I had all the way

home and I prayed to God to excuse my dishonesty and lying for this once. I there promised that if God would get me clearly over this, I would never repeat such action but would break off with sin thenceforth. My wickedness prevailed and I told the falsehood, and was detected by my master. A gracious God did not get me safe through. I soon concluded that my theft was known to the whole village. I concealed myself from all as much as I could, and was so overwhelmed with shame that it was a considerable time before I went out.

It may seem strange to us today, when standards of conduct are often so different, that Carey should be so affected by what some would call a trivial offence. Money had a much higher value then and a shilling would probably be equivalent at least to twenty-five pence today. Be that as it may a theft, for that was what William's action amounted to, is a theft whatever the value. At that time, it could be punished by death and many people suffered this penalty for stealing very small sums of money.

Carey's employer could not tolerate a lie, and William expected to have his apprenticeship cancelled and to incur his father's anger. Fortunately this did not happen, for Clarke Nichols had his virtues as well as his vices, but it made a lasting impression on William and what was more, it emphasised his need of a Saviour. Yet, although he was dissatisfied with his present attitude and beliefs, he hardly knew what he wanted and did not then realise that he needed a change of heart, or a rebirth.

But he had become a seeker, and Jesus said:

'Seek and ye shall find, knock and it shall be opened unto you.'

While he was in this unsettled state, John Warr persuaded him to go to the prayer meeting at Hackleton, a big step for the young man who had been brought up to despise those who had moved away from the Anglican church. But he was impressed by the earnestness of those present and his uneasiness with his own situation grew. Hoping to find some solution he went three times on Sundays to the parish church and to the Hackleton prayer meeting on weekday evenings. He had been confirmed but this does not seem to have impressed him greatly.

He tried to solve his problem by deciding to give up swearing and lying and the other sins to which he was addicted. He tried private prayer but his prayers were formal and meaningless. It was a long hard struggle and a time of great unsettlement.

His thirst for knowledge continued. He browsed among the books in the shoemaker's house and was particularly interested in a Bible which had Greek words interspersed in the text. Languages had always fascinated him and he was determined to learn what these Greek words meant. He pored over the Bible not, at this time, to find peace of mind, but intent on meticulously copying the Greek words.

It is interesting to observe how often the most unlikely people contributed to Carey's knowledge. In this case it was Tom Jones, a weaver in William's home village, who was able to help him. Tom had intended to be a doctor but although he had a good education he failed to qualify because of his bad habits. When Carey appealed to him for help in understanding the Greek words, he brushed up his knowledge of the language and before long Carey was beginning to interpret the words written into the text of the shoemaker's Bible.

Just as Carey, the boy, had said to his mother – 'If I begin a thing I must go through with it,' so now he was determined to use every endeavour in his search for God. He was nearly eighteen years of age when he took a decisive step towards this by giving up attendance at the parish church in favour of the nonconformist's meeting house. This was the direct result of a sermon preached on the text: 'Let us go forth, therefore, unto him without the camp, bearing his reproach.' Although for some time Carey had been attending weeknight prayer meetings, the preacher's message now seemed to be telling him to throw in his lot entirely with the once despised dissenters. It was a hard struggle for him and he must have known that his parents would not approve, but this was a step he had to take. He must follow where God was leading. From that time he always attended the nonconformist services.

A few months later another event occurred to change the current of his life. Quite unexpectedly Clarke Nichols died and Carey's apprenticeship came to an end. There was evidently no difficulty in finding other employment for within a few days he was engaged by Thomas Old, a shoemaker in Hackleton.

Events were certainly shaping Carey's life for the future. Before he had been a week in his new job he met Thomas Scott, a young clergyman and a biblical scholar, who visited Mr. Old's shoemaking establishment. His conversation greatly influenced and helped Carey and whenever he had the opportunity he asked questions and joined in the discussion with eagerness. Mr. Scott was considerably impressed by the younger man and said, prophetically:

'He will prove no ordinary man.'

Carey could never name any specific time when he

became a fully committed Christian, but he often went to the church where Mr. Scott preached, and step by step his search after truth was rewarded. Forty years later he wrote:

'If there be anything of the work of God in my soul I owe much of it to his [Dr. Thomas Scott's] preaching when I first set out in the ways of the Lord.'

In characteristic style, having begun to seek, he went right through until he came to know and accept Christ as his Saviour and Lord. Then he wanted others to have the same experience.

3

Preacher and Schoolmaster

CAREY WAS NOT YET TWENTY WHEN HE FELL IN LOVE with Dorothy Plackett, his employer's sister-in-law. He was earning a very small wage as a journeyman shoemaker. He was married when he had only been in the employ of Mr. Old for two years.

Unlike her husband, Dorothy was lacking in education being unable to sign her name in the parish register after her marriage. But they were happy together in the first two years of married life. William was glad to have his own home, a small cottage in Hackleton, about five and a half miles south of Northampton, and especially glad to have his own garden.

Very soon they had their first child, a daughter, whom they named Ann. But their happiness did not last. Before she was a year old both she and her father caught a fever. It was a sad and anxious time for her parents. William, desperately ill himself, watched anxiously as his child became weaker and weaker, unable to fight the fever at such a young age. It was a great grief when she died and this doubtless delayed her father's recovery, for he was ill for another eighteen months. The sorrow over the loss of his child, and the illness he suffered, combined to make him become bald when he was only twenty-two and for some time he had to wear a wig. It was an ugly one which he later threw overboard on his journey to India.

Six months after the loss of their child they suffered another bereavement. Thomas Old unexpectedly died at an early age, and William Carey was left with the responsibility of carrying on the business. Not only was he dependent on its success for the livelihood of his family, but he felt a responsibility to provide for the widow and her four children. To make matters worse, a customer cancelled his order when the work was practically completed. The winter was a hard one, and Carey had to tramp miles through snow and slush trying to get orders. But trade was poor and he was forced to purchase and repair secondhand boots in order to keep his family. He advertised for these on the board which he printed and hung on his shop door. This board has been preserved and is kept at Regent's Park College, Oxford.

In spite of the ever present problem of making provision for those who depended on him, Carey continued with his language studies. He learned Hebrew from neighbouring ministers, borrowing books from them, and began to read his daily portion of the Bible in Latin, Greek and Hebrew. It is astonishing how much he crammed into these early years, and what ability he had to acquire so many other languages, for he also learned Dutch from a book he found in an old woman's house, and French from a book he managed to buy. Italian was another of the languages he learned. Reading was his absorbing occupation and he always had a book propped in front of him when he was working. He had few of his own and sometimes went without food so that he might buy more.

Meanwhile he had become known as a preacher. Starting at Hackleton he was then invited to preach to the dissenters in the village where his father was still parish clerk and schoolmaster. This was something of an embarrassment to Edmund Carey, who sat in a special seat beneath the pulpit at the parish church, intoning the amens.

William's preaching was so appreciated by the congregation he was invited to preach on his regular monthly visits home. Although neither of his parents could agree with his action in joining the nonconformists, his mother could not hide her pride in her eldest son when a neighbour told her he would make a very great preacher.

Hackleton, where Carey lived, was about ten miles from Pury, and there was no public transport in those days. Even had there been, Carey would not have had the money to pay for it. There is no doubt about his poverty, for when he attended an Association meeting at Olney, after a six-mile walk, he had no money to buy himself a meal. Here, however, he met some people from Earls Barton, a village six miles from Hackleton, in a north-easterly direction. They invited him to preach at their meeting place. This he did with so much acceptance that he was invited to preach there once a fortnight, and he continued to do this for three years, tramping the six miles each way.

His favourite sister, Mary, generally known as Polly, did not go to hear him preach in Pury. She seems, at that time, to have been as much distressed by his leaving the Anglican church as any of the family, and this must have been a great disappointment to her brother. She does tell, however, some years later, when writing about this period of their lives, that their father went secretly to hear him and was evidently satisfied with his son's ability to preach.

William had not seriously considered the question of baptism, but now, from his continued study of the Bible, he became convinced that believer's baptism was the true way of witnessing for Christ. Typically, once having decided that this was the right way for him, he acted. Though not a member of a Baptist church, he had met a number of Baptist ministers in the different meetings he had attended and, on October 5th, 1783, one of them, the younger Mr. Ryland, baptised him in the River Nen, which runs below the ruined walls of Northampton Castle. The service of baptism took place at six o'clock in the morning, and again Carey had a five-mile walk to get there.

About this time he moved his cobbler's shop across the fields to Piddington, taking a cottage near the one where he had started as an apprentice to Clarke Nichols. We are not given the reason for this, but one might assume that it was less costly, for his business was not thriving. He had to sell off some of his stock and tramp miles to sell the shoes he made or mended. The people at Earls Barton were only able to pay a very small fee for his preaching. In fact, he was in such poor circumstances at this time that his younger brother, Tom, came to his aid, giving what he could spare from his meagre savings, and the people at Pury took a collection for him.

Another of his concerns was his health. He worked early and late to make a good garden, but beyond the garden the land was low lying and, in damp weather, it became a misty swamp. His health became affected again by the results of his earlier fever, and he found it increasingly difficult to earn enough to keep his family fed and clothed. He could no longer afford to continue preaching at Earls Barton, where he was given so little it did not cover the shoe leather he wore out in his walks to and from the church.

Then, when his prospects for the future seemed about as poor as they could be, he received a call to preach at Moulton, five miles from Northampton. This call came just as the schoolmaster at Moulton was leaving, and Carey saw that, if he opened his own school there, he would be able to supplement the fee of sixteen pounds a year which was all the church could offer him.

He now seemed to be launched on a new career. The cottage he took at the far end of the village, was built for a shoemaker and he intended to continue with his work. With teaching, shoemaking and preaching he had a busy time, especially as he felt the need to give considerable time to study, though he also found it possible to make a garden. During this year Felix, his first son was born.

Carey did not find the school an easy task at first, for he had difficulty in maintaining order. There were some subjects, such as geography, history, science and natural history which presented little difficulty, for this was where his interests had been since he was a boy. We can imagine him teaching about the horrors of the slave trade and the needs of people in distant lands. The discoveries of Columbus and Cook's explorations he had followed from boyhood and now he would tell the boys in his school of the voyages Cook had made to the South Seas, and how he had landed on coral beaches. He would tell of the strange people who lived there, so unpredictable that they might welcome him with gifts and rejoicings, or shoot at him with their poisoned arrows. He would describe their cannibal feasts and that last voyage when Captain Cook had been brutally attacked and killed.

To assist his teaching, and also for his own visual appreciation of the position, he made a big coloured wall map showing every nation in the known world, putting in the islands Cook had discovered and the populations and religions of the different places. He stitched together coloured pieces of leather to form a globe.

Teaching his scholars of these things increased the intensity of his own desire that the churches in England should send missionaries to teach the peoples of the world about the love of God and his will for men. Whatever Carey's abilities as a schoolmaster were — and some biographers suggest it was not a calling for which he was fitted — this is the sort of thing he could not fail to impart because it was all so vitally important to him. More and more his studies had led him to feel great concern that people of all creeds and colour should have the Gospel preached to them, but even Christian people saw no need for this.

Although his mind had become absorbed by the missionary vision, he did not neglect the church at Moulton. Indeed, his missionary zeal only seemed to increase his desire to win others for Christ in the situation in which he was placed.

He had been preaching fairly regularly since he was eighteen, but he had not been ordained. When he had served for two years at Moulton as the local preacher, the church invited him to become their minister. Three of the well-known Baptist ministers in the Northampton Association — Fuller, Sutcliff and Ryland, who had baptised him — took part in his ordination service. William Carey, the cobbler, was now a recognised Baptist minister. The only thing that grieved him was the death of his mother shortly before his ordination. She would have been proud of her son that day.

During the early years of Carey's preaching he was responsible for leading his two sisters, Polly and Ann, to a knowledge of Christ's love for them. Later, when Polly was only twenty-five, she became paralysed, but although she was an invalid for the rest of her life, she was a wonderful example of a Christian triumphing over suffering. Throughout her brother's life she was his constant correspondent and prayerful supporter. Another event which pleased him at this time was the baptism of his wife, though she did not share his missionary fervour.

He preached three or four times a week at Moulton besides preaching in the surrounding villages, and many were brought to Christ through his ministry. The congregation had been small when he first began to preach at Moulton, but in the four years which he spent there the membership so increased that the meeting house had to be enlarged.

As a young probationer minister he attended meetings at Northampton. When the public meetings were over and the ministers were sitting chatting among themselves, Dr. Ryland, a well-respected older minister (father of the Ryland who had baptised Carey) invited one of the younger men to suggest a subject for discussion. This was a challenge to Carey, one of the youngest and most recently appointed ministers, with no college training as most others present had received. Many of the ministers had long and wide experience in interpreting God's word. Yet here was Carey's opportunity to persuade his fellow ministers of the importance and urgency of the missionary cause.

He rose to the challenge, though not without some nervousness, and proposed that they might consider 'whether the command given to the apostles to teach all nations was not obligatory on all succeeding ministers to the end of the world, seeing that the accompanying promise was of equal extent'.

He anticipated some raised eyebrows that he, a newcomer to the ministry, should propound such a question. What he was not prepared for was the remark which has been attributed to Dr. Ryland:

'Young man, sit down. When God pleases to convert the heathen he'll do it without your help or mine.'

Whether or not this was actually said — and Dr. Ryland's son denies it — the suggestion was greeted with strong opposition and the young man who had proposed it was regarded as somewhat presumptuous. Carey came away from the meeting very disturbed by the attitude of his colleagues, but opposition and indifference to the need only made him the more determined to do something about it.

He talked about it, preached about it and prayed about it. Polly says:

'He was remarkably impressed about heathen lands and the slave trade. I never remember his engaging in prayer, in his family or in public, without praying for those poor creatures.'

Whatever else the Northampton meeting achieved, it made Carey sure of his vocation and he declared his own willingness to take the message abroad. But first he had to convince others of the need for this.

4

Missionary Enthusiast

ALTHOUGH CAREY NOW FELT CONVINCED THAT HIS REAL work lay across the seas in one of the South Sea Islands which his hero, Captain Cook had discovered, there was yet another cause needing him first.

Until this time (1789) he had always lived and worked in villages. Now he received a call from the Harvey Lane Church at Leicester, which was then a country town. From a material point of view it would be to his advantage to accept, the church at Moulton having been able to give him only a very inadequate salary. But this was not the prime consideration for Carey, in spite of the fact that he now had three sons — Felix, William and Peter — and increased financial responsibilities. What did concern him was the decline of that particular church. Here was an opportunity to bring men back into God's loving care; to build up a church at home while waiting to be called to work overseas.

Both Carey and the church at Moulton made this a matter of prayer and, in May 1789, he accepted the new appointment. Having built up and enlarged one church he was now starting to do the same thing all over again. It was a difficult task, calling for courage, initiative and, most of all, dedication. Carey, the missionary enthusiast, still with that determination he had as a boy, faced it with the intention of seeing it through.

Although the church at Leicester was able to pay him more than he had received at Moulton, he was still poor and he still needed to keep school. With school hours taking his time from nine to four in winter and five in summer, he had to be up early in the morning and work late at night to study and prepare his sermons. He had accumulated a fair collection of books and he now had the advantage of a good library near at hand. As at Moulton, he not only preached in his own church but, with the true missionary spirit, he preached in the surrounding villages where people flocked to hear him, his congregation often numbering a hundred.

He was greatly saddened, during his second year in Leicester, by the death of his baby daughter, Lucy. This was the second daughter who had died in infancy. In spite of personal sorrows and a busy life he continued to talk about and develop his interest in people in other lands. Before he left Moulton he had met Mr. Potts, a Birmingham man who shared his interest. Hearing that Carey had started gathering material for a book on the obligation to send missionaries to such people, he urged him to get on with it and gave him ten pounds towards the cost of publishing it.

By the time Carey had completed his *Enquiry*, as it became known, it had developed into a book of eighty pages, a facsimile copy of which was published as recently as 1961. Its lengthy title was typical of publications produced in the eighteenth century.

AN

ENQUIRY

into the

OBLIGATIONS OF CHRISTIANS

to use means for the

CONVERSION

of the

HEATHENS

in which the
Religious State of the Different Nations of the
World, the Success of Former Undertakings,
and the Practicability of Further Undertakings,
are considered

BY WILLIAM CAREY

He based this on the text from Paul's letter to the Romans:

> For there is no difference between the Jew and the Greek: for the same Lord over all is rich unto all that call upon him. For whosoever shall call upon the name of the Lord shall be saved. How then shall they call on him in whom they have not believed? and how shall they believe in him of whom they have not heard? and how shall they hear without a preacher? And how shall they preach except they be sent?

It seems almost incredible that he should have found the time to think out and write down in orderly fashion the arguments he wished to put forward for taking the gospel to the different races of people throughout the world. Here was a man, brought up in obscurity in a small village, mainly self-educated and earning barely sufficient to keep his wife and three children, daring to plan a world-wide campaign for God.

He knew all the arguments against world missions, and in those days, when there were no aeroplanes, no trains and not even steamers, the difficulties of reaching other lands were very real. Yet, Carey pointed out, explorers and traders found it possible to overcome such problems. Other objections, such as the uncivilised state of many of the populations, their cannibalism and barbarism, were known to Carey. While acknowledging the reality of these things, he stated what he truly believed, that these facts made it all the more important that such people should be offered a better and more civilised way of life.

'If we Christians loved men as merchants love money,' he wrote, 'no fierceness of peoples would keep us from their midst.'

The wide variety of foreign languages which would need to be mastered was a challenge rather than a problem to a man of Carey's linguistic ability. He did not forget to deal with the argument that there was still plenty of missionary work waiting to be done at home. His answer to this was that everyone in England was able to hear the Gospel preached if they wished.

His *Enquiry* is the more remarkable because of his review and survey of the extent of the task. It reveals how wide-ranging and comprehensive a study he had made of the different parts of the world, and the individual conditions and customs.

He concludes with the programme which should be adopted and the need to form a Society to carry it out. He elaborates on the necessity to pray, plod, plan and pay, suggesting an average payment of a penny a week from every Christian.

'We have only to keep the end in view and have our hearts thoroughly engaged in its pursuit, and means will not be very difficult,' he writes.

And he concludes:

'Surely it is worth while to lay ourselves out with all our might to promoting Christ's kingdom.'

Carey's *Enquiry* was published in 1792 and on May 31st of that year he was invited to preach at the Northampton Baptist Association meeting held at Nottingham. The sermon he preached on that occasion has been called 'The Deathless Sermon'. It is aptly described if only because its great theme has been the maxim of missionary activity ever since:

'Expect great things from God
Attempt great things for God.'

All through his life Carey lived by this precept and proved the value of it.

His sermon made a terrific impression on all who heard it. His text was from the second and third verses of the fifty-fourth chapter of Isaiah:

Enlarge the place of thy tent, and let them stretch forth the curtains of thine habitations: spare not, lengthen thy cords, and strengthen thy stakes;

For thou shalt break forth on the right hand and on the left, and thy seed shall inherit the Gentiles, and make the desolate cities to be inhabited.'

The New English Bible puts this into the language of today:

> Enlarge the limits of your home,
> Spread wide the curtains of your tent;
> let out its ropes to the full
> and drive the pegs home;
> for you shall break out of your confines right and left,
> your descendants shall dispossess wide regions,
> and re-people cities now desolate.

It was a marvellous opportunity to awaken the churches to a sense of the need and their obligation to spread the good news of God's love abroad. But while many were impressed by the sermon and doubtless made favourable comments on Carey's ability to preach, no one made any attempt to do anything practical about it. One can imagine Carey watching the people talking to each other as they left the meeting, the impression he had made on his hearers already beginning to fade. When even Andrew Fuller, one of the leading young ministers from Kettering, was moving away with no practical suggestion to offer, Carey grabbed him by the arm. With all the earnestness of which he was capable he entreated:

'And are you, after all, again going to do nothing?'

Even at this distance of time one can feel the tenseness of the situation. Fuller, already greatly disturbed by the forcefulness of the sermon, pausing before the younger man's pertinent question, feeling the justification and rightness of the plea, yet knowing the hugeness of the task, wondering whether the time had come to act in faith.

How anxiously Carey must have waited for the response

on which so much depended. He had done his part. Now, if only Fuller would add his weight to the plea, something might be done. When, at last, Fuller gave Carey the answer he wanted, the attitude of some of the other ministers changed.

It was a historic moment when, on Fuller's proposition at the meeting which followed, the Minute was recorded which Carey had longed for:

'Resolved, that a plan be prepared against the next ministers' meeting at Kettering for forming a Baptist Society for the propagation of the gospel among the heathen.'

It was not a quick move in the direction Carey wanted, but it was enough. The period of inactivity was coming to an end.

Four months later, on the evening of October 2nd, 1792, Carey was one of the company of twelve ministers and a theological student from Bristol, who met in the low-roofed back parlour of Widow Wallis's house in Lower Street, Kettering. At that historic meeting the Baptist Missionary Society was founded. It was the first English Missionary Society to be formed to 'propagate the gospel among the heathen', and William Carey was responsible for its foundation. A plaque on the house in Kettering commemorates the fact. Carey was one of the men appointed to serve on the first committee, with Andrew Fuller as Secretary.

For years Carey had worked for this day, trying to convince his fellow ministers of the need for such a society. Now the real work could begin. First, funds were needed and those present at the meeting subscribed between them the sum of thirteen pounds two shillings and sixpence, a small enough sum on which to set out to evangelise the world! Other large sums soon began to come in. Carey promised to give all the proceeds of the sales of his *Enquiry.* With the quickened interest in the subject it was likely to sell well at one shilling and sixpence a copy. This had been the instrument on which the Society was based.

Now Carey prepared himself for the future. He had served the church in Leicester for nearly four years; had seen it rise above its divisions and disputes to become a church worthy of the name. Its membership had increased and there was good reason to hope that this would continue. In these next months the vision of the South Sea Islands must have become very real in his eyes.

But it was not to the South Seas that the attention of the Committee was first directed. It had become known that a certain John Thomas, who had been working in India as a missionary doctor for four or five years, was home trying to gain support for his work. Andrew Fuller had met him and received a glowing account of the prospects of a mission at Malda, among the natives of Bengal. The Committee therefore passed a resolution that:

'A door appeared to be open in India for preaching the gospel to the heathen and that Mr. Thomas be invited to unite with the Society, who would endeavour to procure an assistant to accompany him.'

Without a further thought of the South Seas, Carey immediately offered to go to India with Thomas, feeling that this was God's leading. God's purpose was being fulfilled at last and Carey cared not that he was to be Thomas's assistant. The important thing was to do God's will and bring his love to the people who did not know it.

When, a little later, Thomas arrived at the meeting, and

heard the news, both men were overcome with emotion and the pact was sealed. Carey and Thomas were appointed the first Baptist Missionary Society's missionaries to India.

5

Delays and Disappointments

ONCE THE DECISION WAS MADE, AND CAREY WAS committed to go to India, his personal problems began. First he had to break the news to Dorothy, his wife. He must have known that she would not be happy about it, for she had never travelled far from home. Her people had lived close to one another for a hundred years. She did not share his concern for people of other lands, and she had three sons, all under eight years of age and another child expected. Equally, she must have been well aware of her husband's great desire to spread God's word in other lands. Half anticipating, yet dreading this development, she doubtless tried to turn her thoughts away from the possibility, hoping the day of decision would never come — that something would happen to keep him at home.

Small wonder, then, that when the news was broken to her she could not accept it. Why, oh why, she must have asked him, did he have to do this when he was engaged in such good work building up the church at home? Most of all, why expose her young family to the dangers of crossing the sea to a strange land where the food would be so different and the peoples unfriendly? She would have known what happened to Captain Cook and doubtless feared this could happen to them. She feared, too, that William's health would suffer.

All this must have been very worrying for Carey. He tried to reason with her, but to no purpose. She could not and would not yield. Stability and home, her children and her state of health with the babe on the way, seemed to her good and sufficient reasons why he should give up this idea.

But to Carey, the devout student of scripture, God's commands were to be put first, even before home and family. He had set his hand to the plough and he could not turn back. Having begun a thing he must see it through. And did not Jesus tell his followers that they must love and obey him more than their father and mother, wife and children?

That was how Carey had to leave the matter, but he hoped and prayed that, as the time of departure drew nearer, Dorothy might change her mind.

His father was just as disturbed when he received his son's letter telling of his decision.

'Is William mad?' he exclaimed, after reading the letter, though later he came to understand, if not to rejoice in the work his son was accomplishing.

Then the church in Leicester had to be told. It was not easy for them to understand that they must part with the minister who had done so much to build up their church, and at first they too rebelled, though more in sadness at their loss than in anger. Then one of the members reminded them how their minister had taught them to care for Christ's kingdom, reminded them too, of their missionary prayer meetings.

'And now,' he said, 'God is bidding us make the sacrifice which shall prove our prayers' sincereness. Let us rise to his call, and show ourselves worthy. Instead of hindering our pastor, let us not even be content to let him go; let us send him.'

These were brave words and they had their effect.

It was in January 1793 that Carey accepted the call, and it was arranged that they should sail for India in April of that year. Andrew Fuller suggested that Carey should give up his school and spend the intervening time in visiting the churches, preaching and raising funds for the task ahead. Thomas also did this.

Throughout this time Carey continued in his endeavours to persuade his wife to go with him, but he could not move her. He then decided to take his eldest son, eight-year-old Felix, and to return for Dorothy and the other children after a few years, when he hoped to have overcome the initial difficulties and have somewhere settled for them to live. Meanwhile he arranged for the family to return to their native village of Piddington. He sold up their Leicester home and settled them in a cottage with Dorothy's sister, Kitty.

The farewell services to the two missionaries were held on March 20th, 1793, in the chapel which Carey had served so well during the past four years, Harvey Lane, Leicester. In that time the membership had doubled and the church had been enlarged by the addition of a gallery to accommodate the large congregations. The church was crowded when Andrew Fuller gave the charge to Carey and Thomas at the end of the day's services, taking as his text:

'Peace be unto you, as my father hath sent me, even so send I you.'

He went on to tell the departing missionaries the objects they must keep in view, the directions they must observe, the difficulties they must encounter and the reward they might expect.

This was another milestone in Carey's life. It marked the end of his struggle to prepare himself for this great work to which he was now committed. Difficulties he knew there would be, but he would face them as they arose, knowing that it was God's work and he would supply the power.

Before they left the church that night, the six men now on the Committee of the Society — Ryland, Sutcliff, Hogg, Fuller, Pearce and Carey — made a pact with each other, the five who were remaining at home promising that 'they should never cease till death to stand by him' (Carey). Andrew Fuller later described how he felt about this:

> Our undertaking to India really appeared at its beginning to me somewhat like a few men who were deliberating about the importance of penetrating a deep mine which had never before been explored. We had no one to guide us; and, while we were thus deliberating, Carey as it were, said:
>
> 'Well, I will go down if you will hold the rope.' But before he descended he, as it seemed to me, took an oath from each of us at the mouth of the pit, to this effect, that 'whilst we lived we should never let go the ropes.'

Only one thing marred the joy of that day for Carey — the imminent parting with his wife and family. But this now seemed inevitable. If other men made this sacrifice when going abroad in search of commercial profit, he could do it for God.

Thomas had obtained a passage on the *Earl of Oxford*, a boat on which he had twice sailed as ship's surgeon. They had not been able to obtain the licence which was required, but the Captain, knowing Thomas, had agreed to take them without this. But Carey was worried. It was well known that the East India Company did not want missionaries in India, and they had the power to refuse them entry. He consulted John Newton, a rector of a nearby parish, asking what he should do if the East India Company sent them home again because they had no licence.

'Conclude that your Lord had nothing there for you to accomplish,' came the reply. 'If he have, no power on earth can prevent you.'

Shortly before they set sail Carey met William Ward, a printer from Derby. Carey talked to him about the translations of the Bible he hoped to accomplish in India. Ward showed such interest that, before they parted, Carey said to him:

'I hope, by God's blessing, to have the Bible translated and ready for the press in four or five years. You must come and print it for me.'

Neither man ever forgot that conversation and later Ward acted on it.

At last the day came to set sail. Very few friends were there to see them off on this momentous mission. The boat sailed slowly out of the harbour and set her sails towards the Solent, and Carey felt a deep satisfaction and thankfulness to God that at last his kingdom was to be spread abroad among the nations. Then they had their first delay. The ship dropped anchor at Motherbank, in the Solent. French privateers were in the area. There was to be a six-week delay while the travellers waited for a convoy to guard them. The delay was disappointing and frustrating as the passengers prepared to go ashore and await the arrival of the convoy. Carey and Thomas decided to go to Ryde, in the Isle of Wight, where living was cheaper than it was in Portsmouth.

At that time Ryde consisted of two villages — one housed the fisher folk by the sea, and the other was a very small cluster of gentlemen's seaside houses. Union Street united the two villages. Carey made arrangements for his party to stay in three of the small fishermen's cottages which were then fronting the sea. This is now known as Castle Street, which no longer fronts the sea, shops and houses having been built in front of it. When Carey was staying there he said there were so few shops that he could not even buy a sheet of notepaper.

As recently as 1954 a bathstone plaque was fixed to the upper part of number forty. An East Indiaman in full sail is sculptured at the top. Engraved underneath are these words:

WILLIAM CAREY
1761–1834
Missionary
and Bible Translator
stayed in this cottage
in 1793
awaiting a ship for India
This plaque was affixed in 1954

There is an interesting story behind the erection of this plaque which, to the best of the author's knowledge, has not yet been recorded in any book on Carey. An Indian High Court Judge, Mr. Beeby, had come to Ryde to retire. His father had known Carey when he was in India and he had often told his son the story of the missionaries' frustrated stay in Ryde and what followed. The cottage in which Carey stayed in Ryde and the one each side of it, was purchased by Mr. Mollart-Rogerson, who lived next door to Mr. Beeby. This was in 1930–32. Twenty years later, Mr. Mollart-Rogerson heard that the terrace of cottages would have to be demolished. He contacted Rev. Walter Fancutt, then the minister of Ryde Baptist Church, as a result of which the Ryde Borough Council agreed to restore the three cottages and maintain them, letting number 40 to a suitable tenant, and using the other two as a store and first-floor flat. Mr. Fancutt then arranged for the plaque to be put up and it was unveiled, at the Isle of Wight Spring Meetings of the Baptist Union, by Mrs. Evening, the wife of the President of the Southern Baptist Association. Ernest A. Payne, General Secretary of the Baptist Union of Great Britain and Ireland, spoke outside the house and then preached in the Baptist Church. The Mayor and Mayoress of Ryde, the Town Clerk and members of Ryde Borough Council, attended the ceremony.

Carey's enforced stay on the Island, which, in view of later events, could so easily have been the end of the voyage, was thus remembered. Looking at the plaque today one is reminded of the indomitable determination of the great man whom it commemorates.

In Carey's case this frustrating delay had one very great

advantage when he received news from Dorothy that he had another son. His reply, written on May 6th, suggests that Dorothy was even now trying to persuade him to give up his mission. It is quoted in full because it throws light on their close relationship and William's strong sense of his calling:

I have just received yours, giving me an account of your safe delivery. This is pleasant news indeed to me: surely goodness and mercy follow me all my days. My stay here was very painful and unpleasant, but now I see the goodness of God in it. It was that I might hear the most pleasing accounts that I possibly could hear respecting earthly things. You wish to know in what state my mind is. I answer, it is much as when I left you. If I had all the world I would freely give it all to have you and my dear children with me, but the sense of duty is so strong as to overpower all other considerations; I could not turn back without guilt on my soul . . .

Yesterday I preached twice at Newport, and once in the country. This place much favours retirement and meditation; the fine woods and hills and sea all conspire to solemnise the mind, and to lift the soul to admire the Creator of all. Today I dined with Mrs. Clark (a former member of his Leicester Church), at Newport, and Felix found Teddy Clark one of his old playfellows, which pleased him much. He is a good boy, and gives me much pleasure. He has almost finished his letter, and I intend to add a little to it. He has been a long time about it, and I question whether you can read it when it comes . . .

I shall be glad to hear of you, and how you do, as often

as possible. We do not know when we shall go, but expect it will be in a week at farthest. Tell my dear children I love them dearly, and pray for them constantly. Felix sends his love. I look upon this mercy as an answer to prayer indeed. Trust in God. Love to Kitty, brothers, sisters, etc. Be assured I love you most affectionately. Let me know my dear little child's name.

I am, for ever,
Your faithful and affectionate husband,
William.

He heard later that Jabez was the name Dorothy had chosen for their son.

A few days before the convoy was due to arrive, the Captain of the *Earl of Oxford* regretfully told Thomas and Carey he could not allow them to continue the journey. He said he had received an anonymous letter warning him that he would lose his command of the vessel if he took them to India.

This was a terrible blow to Carey especially, and he believed it was caused by Thomas's debts. He had told the Committee quite candidly that he was in debt, but it was only after they had begun their voyage together that Carey discovered to what extent he was involved, and that his creditors were pressing him for payment. In very many ways Thomas was a good and generous man. He cared about people and was so eager to win them for Christ that he had spent two periods in India doing this. He was, in many ways, a good colleague for Carey, though somewhat unpredictable. But he was no good at estimating costs and, most unfortunately, frequently overspent and got into debt. It shamed and humiliated Carey when Thomas's creditors sought him out hoping to receive payment before he left the country.

Sadly the two men removed their luggage from the ship which was to have taken them to India. Thomas went to London to try and trace the writer of the anonymous letter. When he returned, after an unsuccessful trip, the convoy had arrived and he and Carey unhappily watched their ship moving away under escort without them.

It was a sad and bitter moment for Carey, but he would not believe this was the end of the mission. He remembered Newton's words:

'If God has something for you to accomplish nothing on earth can stop you.'

How often Carey and others who have a complete, unwavering trust in God have proved the truth of this.

Carey also believed that God depends on man to play his part, and with that in mind the two men left their luggage at Portsmouth and set off by coach for London. Here Carey spent the day discussing with friends their best plan of action, while Thomas went searching for another ship bound for India. To his great delight he discovered that a Danish vessel – the *Kron Princessa Maria* – was leaving Copenhagen for England en route for India and berths were available.

With his usual laissez-faire Thomas did not worry about the fact that the cost of the passage was far greater than they could afford. He booked a passage for himself, for Carey and for Felix.

6

Voyage to India

FROM LONDON CAREY AND THOMAS WENT TO NORTHAMPTON. Carey was overjoyed at this fresh turn of events and hoped there might yet be a chance to persuade his wife and family to go with them. He was confident that the Missionary Society would raise the additional money.

His hopes were in vain as far as Dorothy was concerned, and this second parting seemed harder to bear than the previous one. Thomas was so concerned about this that he decided to take a hand in the matter. After telling her the effect of her decision on her husband she at last gave in and said she would be willing to go if her sister would go with her. It speaks well for Kitty, the sister with whom Dorothy was living, that she agreed, with only a day's notice, to pack up her home and join the party for India.

As for Carey, he was so overjoyed at this response that the money which would have to be raised seemed a small matter.

Fuller and Ryland, though concerned at the extra funds now required, were delighted that these arrangements had been achieved. Subscriptions to the Society were steadily coming in and the missionaries were allowed another two hundred pounds for the passage. Fuller was especially pleased that now they could be sent with an easy mind because no licence would be required for travel on a foreign vessel.

The feelings of the little company of people who set off the next day to begin this long and untried journey must have been very mixed. Carey and Thomas were confident that God, who had begun this work, would see them through to the end. The solution of the problems with which they had been confronted at the outset was an indication that 'with God all things were possible' and Carey was acting on the truth of the maxim he had preached at Nottingham — 'Expect great things from God, attempt great things for him.'

The womenfolk must have been concerned with the practical problems of coping, on such a voyage, with four boys all under eight years of age, one only a baby. The difficulties of finding somewhere suitable to live in a strange land, and the kind of people they would be living among were a constant source of discussion. Dorothy was concerned, as most mothers would be, about the different kind of food and whether it would suit the children. Small wonder that she was apprehensive when, the very next day, they set off in two post-chaises for London. For the boys it was a great adventure. For their father, the beginning of his life's work.

Thomas had his own problems to face. He had booked passages for three, and now there were eight counting the baby. Would the ship be able to accommodate so many at this late hour? But Thomas was a man of optimism and always hopeful that things would work out somehow. He knew that, even with the additional money which had been granted them, there was insufficient to meet the normal fares for eight people — four adults and four children — but he had his plans about that. When they reached London he went to the shipping office and persuaded the company to allow him and Dorothy's sister to go as ship's servants, leaving Carey and his family to occupy the berths for which they had the money to pay. With that agreed they set off on the next part of their journey.

Thomas went by coach to Portsmouth to collect the luggage which he and Carey had left there, while the others went by packet boat to Dover to await the arrival of the ship.

Having obtained the luggage Thomas had difficulty in finding someone to take him from Portsmouth to Dover. There was still the threat of a confrontation with French privateers, but at last a fisherman agreed to take the risk under cover of darkness.

All went well and Thomas arrived in Dover before their ship came sailing in, proudly flying the Danish flag. She was a small ship by today's standards, especially for such a journey. She was manned by Danish and Norwegian sailors and there were four other passengers besides Carey's party.

At five o'clock on the morning of June 13th, 1793, the little party boarded her and Carey's heart was full of thankfulness. They were on their way. That evening he entered in his diary:

'This has been a day of gladness to my soul. I was returned that I might take all my family with me, and enjoy all the blessings which I had surrendered to God. This *Ebenezer* I raise. I hope to be strengthened by its every remembrance.'

Felix, who was eight, had already had the experience of a short trip on one ship, but for five-year-old William and four-year-old Peter, this was a completely new experience as, of course, it was for their mother and her sister. Living where they did, in the centre of England, they had not seen a ship before.

The Captain, who was also the owner, was an Englishman who had been an officer in the Danish military service, and was now a Danish citizen. He had adopted the name of Captain Christmas. The name suited him for he was a kindly man. Although not interested in religion, when he learned the object of their journey he insisted that good berths should be provided for the whole party and they should all sit at the Captain's table. This made the voyage much more pleasant for Kitty and for Thomas than they had anticipated.

A good breeze was blowing when they left the white cliffs of Dover at the beginning of their twelve-thousand-mile journey and sailed along the south coast. By the time they reached the Bay of Biscay the breeze had become a squall. The ship was tossed from side to side on mountainous waves which smacked on to the deck. Crockery, tables and chairs were flung against the side of the ship, but she ploughed on, breasting each new wave. The whole party was seasick and as Dorothy Carey lay tossing in her bunk, her unhappy children clamouring for attention, she wished she was back in her own safe world at Piddington.

It was intended that the convoy which had escorted them from Dover should take their mail back to England, but the sea was too rough for it to be transferred from one boat to the other.

At last the storm died away and order was restored on the *Kron Princessa Maria* as she sailed out of the Bay.

Carey found plenty to occupy him during the journey. He conducted services in their cabin twice on Sundays; he studied Bengali with Thomas and spent time in prayer. When they passed through the Tropics he became dangerously ill, another cause of concern for Dorothy. His strong constitution, coupled with his determination, brought him through this illness as it did on many other occasions. While recovering he began thinking about his children's future. He planned to bring them up to be students of languages, one to study Sanskrit and another Persian, for he hoped they would also become missionaries.

Once out of the Bay of Biscay the children adapted themselves admirably to life at sea, even Jabez, the baby, doing well. The wind was favourable, so good, in fact, that they did not put in at the Cape of Good Hope (now Capetown), the captain preferring to take advantage of the additional speed. But they had only reached the southernmost part of Africa when a fierce storm, far worse than that previously experienced, broke upon them. It was midnight. Waves extraordinarily high, washed across the ship, tearing at the rigging and taking everything before them. The ship was tossed up and down on the waves at an alarming angle so that it seemed as though she must capsize. It was an unpleasant experience for the tough seamen but it was terrifying for the women and children. The damage to the ship was so great that it took eleven days to make repairs.

From that time the voyage became pleasant enough, and even Dorothy Carey began to look forward rather than backward. They made good time until they reached the

Bay of Bengal, when it seemed as though their goal was in sight. They had been on the ship for over four months and for the last three had not sighted another ship. It was a long, long voyage and now they were looking forward to being on land again.

Then, when they were within two hundred miles of Bengal, they were caught in cross-currents in the Bay, and were unable to make any headway for almost a month.

Finally they landed in Calcutta on the 11th November, after a voyage lasting five months.

7

Homeless in India

THE PROBLEMS AND SETBACKS WHICH HAD FACED CAREY before he reached India would have daunted a less dedicated man, yet he was full of hope as he landed in Calcutta. Problems and trials he knew there would be, but it was obvious there was a great work to be done. Never had he been in such a crowded place; even London seemed less populated, and this was only one small part of a great country. It saddened him to see the two hundred thousand Asian population crowded into the native quarters in the bazaars, while the many wealthy European merchants and the officials of the all-powerful East India Company were in fine houses set in pleasant surroundings. For the most part they lived in a social round of pleasures, caring little for religion or for moral principles. Not only did they make no attempt to better the conditions or improve the minds of the natives, but they did their best to discourage others from doing so by trying to keep missionaries away from the country.

It soon became obvious to Carey that this was no place in which to start his work. Besides, living was too expensive in Calcutta.

In his *Enquiry* he clearly stated what the missionary's position in the country should be. He must live among the people in the simplest possible manner. This must be their first task, to find the most suitable place in which to settle. It had to be modest because Thomas had assured the Society that one hundred and fifty pounds would be sufficient for their needs for the first year. After that it was Carey's intention that they should support themselves by agriculture or other work.

They found a small house which they could rent in Bandel, a Portuguese settlement on the Hooghli River, thirty miles up the river from Calcutta.

They obtained a boat in which they started visiting the markets and villages in the surrounding area and preached and talked to the people. Thomas could speak the Bengali language and Carey longed for the time when he would be able to do without an interpreter. Thomas had found a *munchi,* or language teacher named Ram Ram Basu, who had been an enquirer in Thomas's earlier days in India, and Carey made good progress with him.

It was not long, however, before they were in financial trouble. Because Thomas already had experience of living in the country, and knew Indian ways, money matters were left to him. When he had told the Missionary Society what it would cost to live in India he had been too optimistic in his estimates, and it soon became obvious that one hundred and fifty pounds was far too small a sum, even for their modest needs. To make matters worse, Thomas had not been accustomed to living economically, and he spent far too freely.

Something had to be done about it. Thomas decided he would go back to Calcutta and set himself up in practice as a doctor. At the same time Carey heard that there was the possibility of a post as an Assistant in the Calcutta Botanical Garden. This was a well-paid position which he was admirably fitted to fill. With this in mind he moved the family back to Calcutta.

Thomas took his share of such money as they had and set up his own establishment in a much grander style than Carey and his family were accustomed to, borrowing to make up the deficiency.

Carey, however, found that the position at the Botanical Gardens had just been filled. This was a bitter blow. Had it been available it would have saved him many anxieties. Now, here he was, homeless in Calcutta, without a colleague and with his wife and eldest son ill with dysentery and he unable to provide for their needs. It was a situation to depress anyone, and for once stout-hearted Carey was dejected.

Once again help came in the hour of their need. A kindly money-lender made over his garden house to them until they could find somewhere more permanent. It was small and inadequate, but they were grateful. Carey never forgot this kind act and later, when his circumstances were very different, he was able to assist the money-lender when he was in need.

Not surprisingly Mrs. Carey and her sister fretted at the lack of a permanent home. But Carey constantly waited upon God for guidance and, in one way or another, he was being led, step by step, to his ultimate goal. This time it was Ram Ram Basu, his *munchi*, who set them moving again. He suggested that they should move to the Soondarbans, a waste jungle to the south-east of Calcutta. The East India Company had salt works nearby and Carey was told they could have the use of one of the Assistant's bungalows while they built their own on land which they could have on lease.

Although Carey knew this was a wild, tiger-infested jungle, he felt he had to take it. It seemed their only hope. Once more their few possessions were packed and they set off by boat in search of their new home. Carey's depression had quickly lifted and he planned to build a modest bamboo house and to cultivate some land. Then they would soon be self-supporting and he would be able to work at the language. Felix was still very ill and the anxiety over the uncertainty of their home, coupled with the illness of her son, became too much for Dorothy Carey. Her nervous system was affected. She felt aggrieved because Thomas seemed to be living in some comfort, if not luxury in Calcutta and she blamed her husband for what was happening to them.

Carey and Ram Ram Basu watched over her and Felix and the rest of the family on the three-day journey. They were afraid to go far from the boat when they moored for fear of tigers.

Again disappointment and near calamity awaited them. The Assistant's bungalow which they had been promised was already occupied, and they had only food left for one more meal.

As so frequently happens in the life of the Christian things which seem calamitous at the time become the means which work out for good. It was so in this case.

On the 6th February, 1794, three months after they had landed in Calcutta, and on the fourth morning of their river journey, they saw another English bungalow. The owner was in the grounds with his gun and dog. It was unusual for a boatload of English people to come this way, and Mr. Short hurried down to meet them. He was not a Christian, and had no interest in missionary work, but when he heard why they were in India and where they were going, he generously invited them into his home and did everything possible for their comfort, especially for the two sick members of the party.

This was a most welcome gesture. For Carey it was a great relief to have somewhere comfortable for his wife and children. Now he could proceed with the building of his bamboo house with less anxiety. It was to be a simple enough structure, just a framework of bamboo covered with grass mats, but it would be their own. The piece of land which he leased was across the river from Mr. Short's house and more than a mile to the north. The heat was more bearable here than in Calcutta at this time of the year and Carey was happy to be settling in a village. With the help of coolies he soon made a clearing in the jungle. He hoped to pay his expenses by selling the trees which had been felled. He built up an earth wall round his land to grow plantains and other fruit and vegetables. Living would be cheap. There was fish in the river and in the forest plenty of hogs and deer. He felt happy as he erected the framework for his house. His wife and son were improving in health and here he would soon learn the language and preach to the people. Altogether there was much to make him thankful.

Yet he knew there were drawbacks. In the river were crocodiles and in the forest cobras and pythons, buffaloes, leopards and boars. Worst of all there were tigers so fierce that twenty men were known to have been killed by them in the previous year. Because of this the village was largely deserted, but as the missionary began to build his house the people began to return to their former homes. They came in their hundreds and Carey wrote that they would soon have three or four thousand people near them — people who needed to be told about the love of God.

Yet it seemed as though Carey and his family were not to lead a settled life. On the first of March, when he was making good progress with his house, he received a letter from Thomas which dramatically altered things for the Carey family, for they were being invited to make yet another move.

George Udney, a Commercial Resident, had been one of Thomas's best friends when he was in India previously. Now Mr. Udney had invited Thomas to become manager of one of his Indigo Factories, and he was offering Carey a similar position in another factory.

Carey did not want to leave the house he had begun to build, or the people who were returning to the village. Yet this letter from Thomas seemed to be God's leading. The more Carey prayed about it the more convinced he became that this was God's will. He would have a settled income, a pleasant home for his wife and family and free the Missionary Society from sending money for his support. In spite of all that had happened in the past Carey knew that Thomas was essentially a good man and he was glad to be given the opportunity of working with him again.

'Nothing yields me more pleasure,' he wrote, 'than the prospect of Mr. Thomas and me being reunited in the work; and particularly as he has, of his own accord, written to me that he knows his conduct at Calcutta was wrong.'

Carey accepted the offer immediately, but he had to wait for money for the journey and for his wife to recover from another attack of dysentery, brought on by the severely hot weather.

On May 23rd they began their three-hundred-mile river journey to Malda.

Dorothy was sorry to leave Mr. Short's comfortable home — the first she had really experienced since arriving in India, almost six and a half months ago. She would miss her sister's companionship too, for Kitty and Mr. Short, their generous host, were in love with each other and were to be married a few months later.

Would this new place to which they were going prove more permanent? Carey was confident, but Dorothy had grave doubts.

8

Indigo Factory

It was no pleasure trip on which the family embarked. The pitiless heat on the tropical sun was almost beyond endurance for Dorothy and the boys. Their only protection was a wooden or straw canopy. Even Carey, whom the climate suited, described himself as feeling 'peevish and uncomfortable'. When they came to the broad expanse of the Ganges they were not prepared for its shallowness in places, and several times found themselves stuck on sandbanks. Then they had a difficult and exhausting task getting themselves off again in the intense heat.

The boys might have thought it fun to be living on a boat when they started, but they became bored and restless as day after day passed, in confined space, with little to interest them in the country through which they passed. A three-week journey under such conditions was extremely trying for all and it is not surprising that tempers became frayed.

With enormous relief they disembarked on the 15th June and made their way to Mr. Udney's house. There they were welcomed by George Udney and his mother. It was a joy for Carey to be entertained in a Christian home and to be able to talk freely about the work he hoped to accomplish in India. That evening he was asked to conduct family prayers and on Sunday, services for the small group of Europeans. The congregation only numbered sixteen, but the preacher was not concerned with numbers in the pleasure and privilege of being able to preach once more. On that day he was reunited with Mr. Thomas. Past problems and mistakes were forgotten, for Carey realised that it was Thomas who had introduced him to Mr. Udney and thereby given him the opportunity to obtain this new position. He was even more gratified when he learned that his salary was to be between two hundred and fifty and three hundred pounds a year, as well as commission on the sales of indigo from his factory. This was staggering news for Carey who, even when doing the three different jobs at one time in England — shoemaking, teaching and preaching — had never earned more than fifty pounds a year. But just as he always regarded preaching as his main task, and shoemaking a necessary occupation to pay expenses, so now he was in India as a missionary, though he would do his utmost to earn his salary and make a success of the factory. Mr. Udney not only understood but encouraged him in this. If Carey could convert his employees to the Christian faith George Udney was happy for him to do so.

Typically, Carey at once wrote to the Missionary Committee at home:

> So now I inform the Society, that I can subsist without any further monetary assistance from them. I sincerely thank them for the exertions they have made, and hope that what was intended to supply my wants may be ap-

propriated to some other Mission. At the same time it will be my glory and joy to stand in the same near relation to the Society as if I needed supplies from them, and to maintain with them the same correspondence.

In the letter he asked them to obtain and send him some agricultural tools and send annually an assortment of garden and flowering trees, fruit, field and forest trees. He promised to pay for these each year. He wanted these to demonstrate how the people of Bengal could become more self-supporting, for he was concerned not only for their spiritual needs but for their better material subsistence.

He was appointed to take charge of the factory at Mudnabati, thirty-two miles north of Malda. Thomas was to be manager of a factory seventeen miles still further north, sufficiently near for them to be able to keep in contact with each other.

Mudnabti was set in a vast plain with small villages among the rice fields. Banyan and mango trees grew here and there and an occasional palm. Although there were wild animals such as boars and buffaloes, they did not cause any trouble. There were crocodiles in the river, but these could easily be seen and avoided. The worst enemies were the snakes and cobras. Very many people died every year from snake bites.

The ground had already been prepared and the seeds sown when Carey arrived. The fine green shoots made a pleasant sight against the hard dryness of the land. The first thing Carey had to do was meet the ninety people of whom he was to be in charge. It was a new kind of life for him, the man who had been cobbler, schoolmaster and preacher. On the face of it this was not what he had come to India to do, but here was a ready-made audience for his message, and an excellent opportunity to become familiar with the language from hearing it spoken by everyone around him. It was also an opportunity to get to know the people, and he knew he must do that if he was to win them for Christ. He must seek to understand them, their religion and the superstitions and practices concerned with it.

He soon discovered that his overseers had been paying the hired coolies far too little in wages and were keeping for themselves a sizeable percentage of even this small wage. He had to use the utmost tact to see that justice was done to the men who were doing the work.

In a month's time, when the rains came, they would be gathering the crop and he had to see that the factory, store and open-air vats were ready. During that month he visited other indigo plants to watch the men bring in the bundles of plants and put them in large vats to ferment and extract the juice from the leaves. He learned how to judge when it was time to let the juice run into a lower vat. He watched the coolies standing in these vats, beating the liquid with bamboo paddles until it changed colour and thickened while the labourers' bodies became as blue as the indigo.

After this process it had to be left for a time before being further processed and cut into cubes, dried and packed for despatch to Calcutta. All this processing Carey quickly learned.

Meanwhile he was continuing to study the language, for he and his family were the only white people. Unfortunately the dialect was different from that which he had learned, and this made for more difficulty. But study was easier here, for now he had a good new two-storeyed house, with spacious rooms and several acres of ground which he intended to make into a fine garden.

Daily he was made more and more aware of heathen customs which were repulsive to him. On the day before their first indigo-making his work-people came to him asking if he would make an offering to their god Kali for good luck. He would have liked to forbid them to make any offering to such a god, but knew that this would be unwise. He took the opportunity of talking about the one true God whom he worshipped. But though he talked and they listened it seemed to make no difference to them and their beliefs.

India has three different seasons — November to February are the cool months. These are followed by the hot months, with dry hot weather until the rains come about July. This rainy season lasts until September and is followed by moist hot weather. The rainy season is known as the monsoon and that is when the crops are cut. This is a trying time for Europeans and Indians alike, and this year was a particularly bad one. Day after day his work-people became ill with fever, so that he could hardly manage to carry on the business. When there came a fine day in the midst of the rainy season, Carey was out in the heat all through the day until the evening. He describes himself at this time as being so fatigued he could not pray.

Ram Ram Basu, Carey's language teacher, was ill for three months. Then, in September, Carey himself went down with a bad attack of fever. The very next day his five-year-old son Peter, had an even more severe and sharp attack, followed by dysentery. Dorothy Carey was in no state to nurse the invalids, being now quite unable to cope with ordinary affairs. All the trials she had been through, the dysentery she had suffered and the fears created in her mind by this unknown and, to her, strange land with its queer practices, proved too much for her.

Though still ill himself William fought for his boy's life, but his efforts were in vain. Five-year-old Peter died.

This was a very sad time for the Careys, made more so by the difficulty of finding anyone to make the coffin or dig the grave. Caste rules were so rigid that no Hindu or Mohammedan could be induced to help with the burial. Four men did eventually agree to dig the grave but they were afterwards treated as outcasts and no one was allowed to eat or drink with them.

This was yet another example of the need for the preaching of the Christian gospel, to take away men's fears and superstitions. But it was a long, hard struggle. There were so many evil and cruel practices performed in the name of religion and all Carey could do at present was to make his voice heard against them.

Among the problems which Carey had to face was that of loneliness. His wife's health was deteriorating and he was the only white man in the district. He had received no letters from England although he had written frequently. Had those who had promised to pray for him — 'to hold the ropes' — forgotten him? It was only later he heard that letters had been written but had miscarried.

Steadfastly he went on with his work. His duties at the indigo factory occupied him fully during the rainy season, when the processing was being carried out. He was earning sufficient money to support himself and his family and even to make monetary contributions to the missionary cause. At the same time he was in the best position to acquire a ready use of the language and to visit in the district which covered about twenty square miles and included about two hundred villages. He travelled in two small boats, one to live in and the other for cooking his food. There were no roads and he walked along the ridged paths between the rice fields from one village to another, visiting the farmers who cultivated the indigo for the factory and the five hundred factory workers who lived in this area.

These formed Carey's congregation. Week by week the numbers attending services increased until he was preaching to as many as six hundred people. Through limitations in his knowledge of the language he was not able to vary his preaching very much, but he was encouraged by the fact that many came who had no connection with the factory. They listened to his message and some came to him for instruction.

Yet what had he achieved in the time he had been in India? Not much it seemed. It was now nearly two years since he had left a thriving church in England and not one Hindu or Mohammedan had become a Christian. In fact, there were no native Christians. Even Ram Ram Basu, who had shown great promise of becoming a Christian, had turned away to heathen practices and had to be dismissed from the mission.

What would the people at home think? With a view to trying to help the committee to understand, he wrote:

> What would three ministers do even in England, supposing it now dark and rude as when Caesar discovered it; supposing them, also, to have the language to learn before they could converse with any; and then to have the Scripture to translate and write out with their own

hands; and this done, to have no other means of making the Scriptures known but preaching; with printing almost totally unknown, and only here and there one able to write. This, brothers, is our case. May it speed your prompt help.

In another letter he wrote:

'I hope you will not be discouraged by our little positive success, but rather regard it as a call to double exertion and to send us more men.'

Yet, just as they had to have a time of seed sowing and preparation before the indigo was produced, so this was a period of sowing the Christian gospel. The harvest would come later, as indeed it did.

Carey had been in India less than three years when he had a pleasant surprise. One morning, when he was sitting with his teacher learning Sanskrit, a new missionary arrived. Thrusting aside his studies Carey welcomed him eagerly. His name was John Fountain, their first recruit. He had come to strengthen Carey in his work and relieve his loneliness.

Their first convert was a man of thirty-eight, a Portuguese who had lived in China and now owned a wax-candle factory at Dinajpur, a little to the north-east of Malda. He became a devoted Christian, building a splendid preaching hall next to his own house for Indians and Europeans. Carey and Thomas regularly conducted services there.

Yet the mission was still without a native convert and Carey decided that hope of planting the Gospel in India might lie with the children, so he started a school. However, this did not succeed because the parents took the children away after a few months so they could start earning. But Carey was a man of ideas. If one thing failed he tried another.

> We have formed a plan for setting up two colleges for the education of twelve youths in each [he wrote]. I had some months ago, set up a school, but the poverty of the natives caused them frequently to take their children to work. To prevent this we intend to clothe and feed them and educate them for seven years in Sanskrit, Persian, etc., and particularly to introduce the study of the Holy Scriptures and useful sciences therein. We also intend to order types from England at our own expense and print the Bible and other useful things in the Bengali or Hindustani languages. We have reason indeed to be very thankful to God for his kind providence, which enables us to lay out anything for him. May our hearts be always ready.

Here was the development Carey had been waiting for. His study of the language had been pursued for this purpose — to print the Bible in the languages of the people so that God's message could come to them through the written as well as the spoken word. That he was intending to buy the types at his own expense when they were already supporting themselves financially, shows just how far their dedication to God's work went. From his own salary of two hundred rupees a month he was saving one-sixth for missionary work.

One of the things which he found most hard to combat was the torture which people inflicted on themselves in the name of their religion. The time of the hook-swinging festival came round and Carey was greatly disturbed to see people dancing with splints of bamboo thrust through their flesh, and then swinging in the air suspended from hooks. This was only one of the practices which Carey had to fight. Another, which he witnessed thirty miles from Calcutta, is best described in his own words. It was the practice known as *sati*:

We saw a number of people assembled on the riverside. I asked for what they were met, and they told me to burn the body of a dead man. I inquired if his wife would die with him; they answered yes, and pointed to her. She was standing by the pile of large billets of wood, on the top of which lay her husband's dead body. Her nearest relative stood by her and near her was a basket of sweetmeats. I asked if this was her choice, or if she were brought to it by any improper influence. They answered that it was perfectly voluntary. I talked till reasoning was of no use, and then began to exclaim with all my might against what they were doing, telling them it was shocking murder. They told me it was a great act of holiness and added in a very surly manner that if I did not like to see it, I might go further off, and desired me to do so. I said I would not go, that I was determined to stay and see the murder, against which I should certainly bear witness at the tribunal of God. I exhorted the widow not to throw away her life, to fear nothing, for no evil would follow her refusal to be burned. But in the most calm manner she mounted the pile, and danced on it with her hands extended as if in the utmost tranquillity of spirit. Previous to this, the relative whose office it was to set fire to the pile, led her six times round it — thrice at a time. As she went round, she scattered the sweetmeats amongst the people who ate them as a very holy thing. This being ended, she lay down beside the corpse, and put one arm under its neck, and the other over it, when a quantity of dry cocoa-leaves and other substances were heaped over them to a considerable height, and then Ghee, melted preserved butter, was poured on the top. Two bamboos were then put over them, and held fast down, and fire put to the pile which immediately blazed very fiercely, owing to the dry and combustible materials of which it was composed. No sooner was the fire kindled than all the people set up a great shout of joy, invoking Siva. It was impossible to have heard the woman had she groaned, or even cried aloud, on account of the shoutings of the people, and again it was impossible for her to stir or struggle, by reason of the bamboos held down on her, like the levers of a press. We made much objection to their use of them, insisting that it was undue force, to prevent her getting up when the fire burned. But they declared it was only to keep the fire from falling down. We could not bear to see more, and left them, exclaiming loudly against the murder, and filled with horror at what we had seen.

9

Reinforcements

IN SPITE OF ALL CAREY'S EFFORTS, THE INDIGO FACTORY was not succeeding. Climatic conditions were against it. He had been managing the Mudnabati Factory for four years when there was a really disastrous flood. Ten days before, everything looked promising; the fields were covered with rice, hemp, indigo, cucumbers and gourds. Then the rains came, heavy even by India's standards. Carey went out by boat but there was no sign of the crops which had seemed so healthy such a short time before. The rivers had overflowed making two large lakes three miles wide and fifty miles long, and the fields were covered with water from two to twenty feet deep. It was a scene to discourage any grower whose livelihood depended on the land.

Yet neither Carey nor Mr. Udney, his employer, despaired. Next year's crop might be better.

Their optimism was not rewarded. Instead of the flood, the next year there was a drought which burnt the crops and dried up the vats. Too much water one year and too little next caused heavy losses, but Carey still felt he could succeed given better seasons.

He had written home for more missionaries to be sent

out, though he had warned the Society that they would not be allowed into India as such. He was registered as manager of an indigo factory. Thomas was allowed because he was a doctor. Now Carey had to find employment for the new colleagues he expected.

With this in mind he bought a small indigo factory at Khidupur, twelve miles to the north and across the River Tangan. It was on higher ground and he hoped it would be free from floods. He planned to pay for it with the profits from the crops, although most men would not have dared to take the risk; faced with all this, and the other difficulties which had gone before, they would have given up. But Carey was not the type to give up. Difficulties were there to be overcome. He was the plodder — the man who, as a boy, had said: 'If I start a thing I must go through with it.' How fortunate the church was to have sent such a man, how fortunate, too, that he was so quick in understanding and translating languages. His children had been a help in this. He wrote:

'My children can speak nearly as well as the natives and know many things in Bengali which they do not know in English.'

On another occasion he said that listening to children is by far the quickest way of learning.

In addition to all his other work he had practically completed translating the New Testament into Bengali. This had all been done in handwriting; a laborious task. The next question was how to get it printed. On making enquiries he found that it would cost four thousand pounds for an edition of ten thousand copies. This was much beyond their means. There was the possibility of a printer. William Ward, whom he met just before going to India, coming out for this purpose. If they could obtain a printing press by the time Ward arrived, the printing of the first New Testament in the Bengali language could begin.

Although Carey knew he had insufficient money to buy such a press, he scanned the advertisements until he saw one advertised for four hundred rupees (about fifty pounds). It was yet another case of having attempted great things for God and now expecting great things from him.

To Carey's delight an English friend (some think it was George Udney) offered to pay for this and for the type. With Ward as the printer, production of the Bengali New Testament could begin.

The future of the mission was full of promise, in spite of the lack of native converts. People at home were realising the need of supporting the missionaries. Andrew Fuller wrote that subscriptions were coming in well, especially from Scotland. Missionaries had been sent to Africa, and other denominations, notably the Congregationalists (now the United Reformed Church) had started the London Missionary Society soon after hearing Carey's first letters from India read by Mr. Ryland. Now, in 1799, the Church Missionary Society had been formed.

When everything else seemed to be going well there came another setback. Mr. Udney decided to close the factory. This was not unexpected after the recent bad seasons. He had spent ten thousand pounds setting up the factories which Carey and Thomas had managed, and they were not bringing in a sufficient return. Thomas had already given up. He was a good medical missionary and preacher but no good in business.

Now that Carey was to lose his well-paid position he

might have to ask the Missionary Society for their financial support for a time. He pinned all his hopes on the new factory he had purchased and made plans to build a house for himself and his family and to make this a centre for their missionary work.

While he was making these plans William Ward arrived. It was a happy day for Carey and tremendously encouraging. Ward was just the man to assist him. He wrote in his diary about his meeting with Carey:

> Sunday, December 1st, 1799, Mudnabati. This morning we left the boat and walked a mile and a half to Carey's house. I felt very unusual sensations as I drew near, after a voyage of fifteen thousand miles and a tedious river passage ... The sight of the house increased my perturbations. At lengths I saw Carey. He is very little changed from what I recollected, rather stouter than when in England, and, blessed be God, a young man still. He lives in a small village, in a large brick house, two-storey, with Venetian windows and mat doors. Fountain lives in a bungalow a quarter of a mile away ... The four boys talk Bengali fluently. Felix is fourteen or fifteen. We arrived in time for the Bengali morning worship. Carey preached at 11.0 in the Hall. I was much moved by the singing. There is a Mission school of about thirty.

The reason for William Ward's perturbations on seeing Carey's house was that he had come to persuade Carey to move to Serampore and make that the missionary centre.

Three other missionaries, with wives and children, had arrived in India with William Ward. They were staying in

Serampore, a port on the river Hooghli, about two hours' journey to the north of Calcutta and on the opposite bank. The whole party had planned to go up country to join Carey, but as they would have to travel through territory under the jurisdiction of the East India Company they were not allowed to go. Ward, however, obtained a Danish passport through the good offices of Colonel Bie, who was in control of the Danish territory, and who lived at Serampore. He had promised the missionaries that if they would make Serampore their headquarters he would see that they had complete freedom to teach and preach and print the Bible.

Sadly, however, Ward had to tell Carey that one of the four, Mr. Grant, had died of fever shortly after they had landed. His widow and two children were in Serampore.

Here was a dilemma for Carey. Could he uproot himself yet again and make a fresh home for his family? It would mean giving up the place he had so recently acquired and losing money on it. The new party of missionaries felt it was God's will that they should settle in Serampore, but they looked to Carey as the leader to make the decision.

It very quickly became obvious to him that they were right, and when he heard that George Udney was being offered a position in Calcutta, Carey knew he had to go to Serampore. The man who was to replace Udney at Malda was opposed to missions. Added to this, the use of a printing press in British Bengal outside of Calcutta had just been forbidden and this would have made it impossible for the Bible to be printed anywhere other than in Danish territory. In Serampore missionaries could be recognised as such and they would be in a district which was more densely populated than anywhere else in the world. In view of all these considerations there was no doubt in Carey's mind about the necessity to leave Mudnabati and go to Serampore.

Once more the Carey family was on the move, but this was to be the last. During the six years he had been in India Carey had gained a vast amount of knowledge of the country and her peoples. He had also acquired a great deal of experience. The Northamptonshire cobbler who was to set up the missionary centre in Serampore was a man of vision. When he decided to purchase a large house standing in spacious grounds, he was thinking of the need to spread the message of God's love not only in India, but in the whole of Asia. From having only his own family to consider and plan for, he now had also the three new arrivals and their families, as well as Fountain and his fiancée, Miss Tidd, who had come out with the other missionaries.

Two of the new missionaries — William Ward and David Brunsden — were single men. Joshua Marshman and his wife, Hannah, had two children, and then there was Mrs. Grant and her two children. In addition to the requirements for living accommodation for this number they needed room for a school and a printing works.

The house which was purchased is described by William Ward:

> The renting of a house, or houses, would ruin us. We hoped therefore to have been able to purchase land and build mat houses upon it, but we can get none properly situated. We have in consequence purchased of the Governor's nephew a large house in the middle of the town for Rupees six thousand, or about eight hundred

pounds; the rent in four years would have amounted to the purchase price. It consists of a spacious verandah (portico) and hall, with two rooms on each side. Rather more to the front are two other rooms separate, and on one side is a storehouse, separate also, which will make a printing office. It stands by the river-side upon a pretty large piece of ground, walled round, with a garden at the bottom, and in the middle a fine tank or pool of water. The price alarmed us, but we had no alternative; and we hope this will form a comfortable missionary settlement. Being near to Calcutta, it is of the utmost importance to our school, our press, and our connection with England.

They planned to live together, having a common purse, and they decided that no one was to work for his individual gain. They agreed to preach and pray in turn, and to take it in turn each month to supervise the affairs of the household. Each had their duties. Carey was in charge of their financial affairs. Marshman and his wife were to start a boarding school. Ward and Brunsden were to work in the printing office.

Once more Carey made a garden — a bigger and better one than he had been able to make before. Out of the two acres of ground he made a Botanic Garden, planting mahogany trees to make a broad walk, known later as 'Carey's Walk'.

They planned their days well. Starting at six o'clock in the morning, Carey spent the first hour in his garden. At seven o'clock Marshman went to his school, while Brunsden and Ward went to the printing office. Felix, Carey's eldest son, was now old enough to help with this, and made himself very useful. Although William was still at school, he spent part of the day learning book binding. They made a break for family worship before breakfast.

Carey spent most of his time studying and translating the language and superintending the printing of the Bible, though time was set aside by all the missionaries for preaching and for corporate and individual prayer for the spreading of the Gospel. On Sundays Carey was often out preaching three times a day and in the cooler season even four times. Later he went on Fridays as well. He always took with him leaflets about the Bible.

An Agreement was drawn up to set out the way the mission and the missionary staff should function, both in India and in relation to the Baptist Missionary Society in England. The Agreement covered the legal and the economic concerns. While the Society at home agreed to provide the main part of the funds, by the end of the first year the income from the schools and the printing office enabled the missionaries to be fully self-supporting and even to have a reserve fund for extension.

The expanded Agreement drawn up by the missionaries in 1805 included the spiritual side of the mission and the attributes necessary for the missionaries. Part of this reads:

> Prayer, secret, fervent, believing prayer, lies at the root of all personal godliness. A competent knowledge of the languages current where a missionary lives, a mild and winning temper, and a heart given up to God in closest religion; these, these are the attainments which more than all knowledge or all other gifts, will fit us to become the instruments of God in the great work of

human redemption. Finally, let us give ourselves unreservedly to this glorious cause. Let us never think that our time, our gifts, our strength, our families, or even the clothes we wear are our own. Let us sanctify them all to God and his cause.

Such was the dedication of these early missionaries. With this selfless spirit the Baptist Missionary Society was established in India.

10

Fight Against Evil

FROM THE TIME CAREY WAS A BOY HE HAD BEEN DEEPLY concerned about cruelty and oppression in all its forms. He had never ceased to pray for the abolition of the slave trade, and he had prayed continually for the enlightenment of the whole world.

In India he saw for himself the cruel practices performed in the name of religion. Most of the people were of the Hindu religion and, as such, were subject to the caste system. Originally, there had been only four main castes; the Brahmins, or priests, being the highest. Then there were the fighting men, the tillers of the soil and, in the lowest caste, the servant or sweeper caste. The outcasts, or untouchables, had an existence little better than animals.

Over the years many more castes crept in, and with these, penalties for losing caste increased and became more severe. With a system such as this, Christ's law of love for one's neighbours could not exist. Any idea of God as a loving father was quite outside the experience of the Hindu. Their gods were idols such as Krishna and Radha, the monkey and the serpent. Just as the caste system had been extended beyond that at first intended, so more and more idolatrous festivals and cruel and evil practices crept into Hinduism, and the Brahmins, who were paid to be present at all of these, became rich and powerful at the expense of the more ignorant.

Ward wrote, in one of his letters from Bengal:

> On landing in Bengal in the year 1793, our brethren found themselves surrounded with a population of heathens (not including the Mahometans) amounting to at least one hundred millions of souls . . . Amidst innumerable idol temples they found none erected for the worship of the one living and true God. Services without end they saw performed in honour of the elements and deified heroes, but heard not one voice tuned to the praise or employed in the service of the one God . . . Amongst these idolaters no Bibles were found; no sabbaths; no congregation for religious instruction in any form; no house for God; no God but a log of wood, or a monkey; no Saviour but the Ganges; no worship but that paid to abominable idols, and that connected with dances, songs and unutterable impurities.

These were the people to whom Carey and his fellow missionaries came to teach a better way—the way of Christ. Yet it was difficult to break the chains which bound them to the caste system and all it entailed. A change of religion meant loss of caste. Those who dared to make such a change were persecuted and disowned by relatives and friends. Little wonder, then, that seven years passed before Carey saw the first convert.

One of the biggest evils was that of child marriage. Men

were employed by parents to find wives for their sons. Without the girl's consent she was bound by a legal agreement to marry the boy selected for her at a time which suited the parents. Until this time she did not even see him.

Another of the Hindu practices which were abhorrent to the missionaries was that of taking the people who were facing death to the banks of the Ganges, which they believed to be sacred, and leaving them there to die. Many mothers made sacrifices to the Ganges by drowning their newly born babies there.

The treatment of lepers was appalling. Carey's second son, William, described a case he actually witnessed without being able to interfere:

> A pit about ten cubits in depth was dug and a fire placed at the bottom of it. The poor man rolled himself into it; but instantly, on feeling the fire, begged to be taken out and struggled hard for that purpose. His mother and sisters, however, thrust him in again; and thus a man, who to all appearance might have survived several years, was cruelly burned to death. I find that the practice is not uncommon in these parts. Taught that a violent end purifies the body and ensures transmigration into a healthy new existence, while natural death by disease results in four successive births, and a fifth as a leper again, the leper, like the even more wretched widow, has always courted suicide.

Who can blame these people when they were being so taught?

It was to show them a better way — the way of God's

love revealed by the sacrifice Christ made once for all men — that Carey and the missionaries devoted their lives.

While he was in India Carey was tireless in his efforts to prevent these practices and to persuade the Government to make laws forbidding them. Despite all Carey's pleas, however, there was considerable hesitancy on the part of the Government to interfere with the practices encouraged by the religion of the people. It was years before many of these evils ceased to exist.

Widow-burning, for instance, was not abolished until 1829, after Lord Cavendish-Bentinck became Governor-General. On Sunday morning, 5th December, 1829, when Carey was preparing to preach, a messenger came with the request to Carey to translate a document into Bengali. It was an Order in Council abolishing *sati* throughout the British dominions in India.

Carey wasted no time. Arranging for someone to take his place in the pulpit, he settled down with his pundit to the task which took him all day. Having protested against this practice for more than twenty-five years, he did not intend to lose even an hour in making its abolition known. In Bengal alone, about six thousand widows had suffered the fate of burning with their dead husbands during the previous ten years.

The teaching and influence of Carey and other missionaries was directly or indirectly responsible for the gradual abolition of many other cruel practices. But the missionaries were to endure many trials of their own before these laws were passed.

11

First Converts

AT ONE O'CLOCK ON THE LAST SUNDAY IN THE YEAR 1800, Carey baptised the first native convert.

Following the service in the English church at Serampore, when William Ward preached the sermon, a group of people, including the Danish Governor of Serampore, stood on the bank of the Hooghli, opposite the entrance to the Mission House. A mixed group, including Europeans, Portuguese, Hindus and Mohammedans, joined in singing a Bengali translation of the hymn by Joseph Grigg:

> Jesus, and shall it ever be,
> A mortal man ashamed of thee,
> Ashamed of thee, whom angels praise,
> Whose glories shine through endless day?

After the singing of the hymn Carey addressed the people in Bengali, explaining that though the Hooghli was a tributary of the Ganges, which the natives regarded as sacred, the water had no special power and was in no way regarded by Christians as sacred. He told them that this act of baptism was the Christian way of demonstrating that those who were baptised had agreed to leave their old sinful ways and rise to a new life in Christ.

Standing on either side of Carey were his eldest son, Felix, now fifteen years of age, and a great help in the printing office, and Krishna Pal, a Bengali carpenter who had, for some time, been coming to the missionaries for instruction. After prayer, Felix went down into the water, where his father baptised him, and then Krishna Pal, the first native convert. It was a joyful day for the missionaries, and especially for Carey. It was Thomas who had been responsible for introducing Krishna to Christ, and, in the event, the excitement and emotion were too much for the missionary and he was unable to attend the service of baptism, or of the candidates' first communion service which followed.

It had been far from easy for Krishna Pal to become a Christian. For sixteen years he had been a *guru*, or Hindu spiritual teacher. He had suffered from ill health and a sense of sin over a long period. Although his health had improved he could not rid himself of this feeling of guilt. Then he heard that the missionaries were teaching that Jesus Christ came into the world to save sinners. This impressed Krishna considerably, but it was an accident that first brought him into close contact with the missionaries.

One morning, when he was about to bathe, he fell down the slippery side of the tank and dislocated his shoulder. A messenger ran to tell Dr. Thomas, who was known to have medical powers. Although he had not finished breakfast, Thomas at once answered the call for help. While he worked on the shoulder he talked of Christ and his power to forgive sins. He gave Krishna Pal a tract which further explained the Christian message. The next day Carey called on the *guru* telling him to come to the Mission House for medicine to relieve the pain in his shoulder.

> I went and obtained the medicine [said Krishna Pal] and through the mercy of God my arm was cured. From this time I made a practice of calling at the Mission House, where Mr. Ward and Mr. Felix Carey used to read and expound the Holy Bible to me. One day Dr. Thomas asked me whether I understood what I heard from Mr. Ward and Mr. Carey. I said I understood that the Lord Jesus Christ gave his life up for the salvation of sinners, and that I believed it, and so did my friend Gokool. Dr. Thomas said: 'Then I call you brother — come and let us eat together in love.' At this time the table was set for luncheon, and all the missionaries and their wives, and I and Gokool, sat down and ate together.

Although accepting an invitation to a meal seems harmless enough to us, it was not so in India. In fact, it was a very courageous action on their part because they were well aware of the consequences. Quickly the news spread that Krishna Pal and Gokool had become Europeans and their troubles began. On their way home they were attacked by a gang of natives. Later a huge crowd of people went to the house of Krishna and Gokool and forcibly took them before the magistrate. He sent them on to the Danish Governor, Colonel Bie, who was friendly towards the missionaries. He was, in fact, a member of the English church and had contributed towards the work of the mission. As soon as he heard the story he told the crowd that Krishna Pal and Gokool had not become Europeans but Christians and not only did he tell their accusers not to harm them, but he set a guard before the houses of the two men to keep them safe.

However, that was not the end of the affair. The crowd were not going to give up so easily. If they were not allowed to hurt them physically they had another way. It was the custom for parents to arrange marriages between quite young children — when they were five and six years old — in fact they could actually be married at that age. Once the contract was made it was unalterable, although the marriage might not take place for some years. Krishna's eldest daughter, though still very young, had been contracted to a Hindu neighbour in marriage. Now the mob seized her and insisted on the marriage being observed, much to her distress, for not only Krishna, but his wife and children had responded to the message of the gospel and she did not wish to marry a Hindu.

It was a sad time for them and, as a result of all the opposition, only Krishna eventually came forward for baptism, Gokool and the women folk saying they would wait a while.

Krishna's conversion and baptism was but the beginning. As he openly admitted he was a Christian and went about with the missionaries, others took notice; some to persecute, but others to seek the same Saviour. Among these was Jaymani, Krishna's wife's sister, who became the first Bengali woman to be baptised. Soon after, Krishna's wife, Rasamayi, came forward for baptism. Gokool's wife had gone back to her father, still fearful of the results of becoming a Christian and this kept her husband back. Krishna and his family had the true missionary spirit. They knew Gokool wanted to join them in Christian worship and, like Andrew, who brought his brother Peter to Jesus, they were not satisfied until they had brought Gokool and his wife to the missionaries for baptism.

How Carey and his fellow missionaries must have rejoiced that at last the Christian church, though small in number, was really established in Bengal. For seven long years Carey had laboured for this day. Often it had seemed as though his work was in vain. Many who appeared to be ready to accept Christ had, when it came to the point of decision, counted the cost and drawn back. Yet Carey had plodded on, believing that once the scriptures were translated, and in the hands of the people, they would speak for themselves. Now that some had dared to become Christians and defy the old superstitions, others followed.

Those who had been baptised had the true missionary spirit. Having experienced for themselves the joy of belonging to Christ, and being freed from superstitions and evil practices, they wanted others to share their experience. They went among their friends in Seramapore and into the surrounding villages, telling the good news of forgiveness and God's love to man.

The missionaries encouraged this and were delighted when Krishna Pal, their first convert, built a native church opposite his own house. When Carey preached the first sermon in this place twenty native people came to hear him, besides Krishna's family. Krishna was thirty-six when he was baptised, only three years younger than Carey. Later he was ordained as a preacher and was the first Bengali hymn writer. One of the hymns he wrote is in the Baptist Church Hymnal. It reveals Krishna's own feelings at this time:

> O thou my soul forget no more
> The friend who all thy miseries bore,
> Let every idol be forgot
> But O my soul forget him not.

The words were translated into English by Joshua Marshman.

Then there was Petumber Singh, an older man of the writer caste. For years he had been a searcher after truth, seeking it through the study of Hinduism and the Brahman teaching, until he was given one of the tracts issued by the Serampore Press explaining the Christian message. Such was his desire to learn more of this Saviour that he set off at once to walk the forty miles to the mission station at Serampore. Before long he was baptised, and another useful life was added to the church. He became a master at the Serampore school and was ordained a preacher.

Although converts were few in number at the beginning, some who had been hesitating, afraid of the consequences of losing caste, became emboldened by the example of the first Christians.

While Carey rejoiced at the way God's work was at last beginning to prosper, it brought its own problems. Would these converts, having so recently discarded their Indian religions, against opposition from their friends and relatives, hold fast? It was such a new way of life for them. Those who showed any sign of becoming suitable evangelists were trained for this work. They were expected to live as the missionaries did, devoting time, talents and money to God's work.

When a high caste Christian brahmin wanted to marry a daughter of Krishna Pal, a new form of marriage service and agreement had to be drawn up. That a Brahmin should marry outside his caste was unheard of and would not have happened outside the Christian church. No Indian was expected to marry one of another caste. But now Carey had the joy of conducting a Christian wedding. It was a great day in the life of the mission.

Not only weddings but funerals had to be provided for, and Carey purchased an acre of land for Christian burial. Gokool was the first of the native Christians to be buried there. When he became ill his neighbours did their utmost to persuade him to have a native doctor, but he refused, saying:

'I want no physician but Christ.'

When they asked how it was that he had to suffer when he had accepted Christ, he said:

'My affliction is on account of my sins. My Lord does all things well.'

Throughout his illness Gokool witnessed for his Master by his immense patience during suffering. He never complained and died happily, with his friends around him singing and praying.

This made a great impression on all who knew him.

'May my mind be as Gokool's was,' they said.

Carey was away at the time of Gokool's death and Marshman decided to set an example to the growing Christian community and to those who were antagonistic to the Christian faith. Knowing the aversion which Hindoos had for a dead body he arranged with Krishna Pal to make the coffin. When Carey's two sons, Felix and William, together with two high caste converts, had joined Marshman in putting the body in the coffin, they themselves bore it to the grave.

Life never flowed smoothly for the missionaries. They had their times of uplift and rejoicing and their times of sadness. More missionaries had volunteered and been sent to India to strengthen the work of the small band of devoted men and women at Serampore, yet there was need for many more. The native Christians who were suitable to serve as evangelists were being placed at strategic centres spreading out from Serampore, and Carey had plans for extending the mission to other parts – Burma and China, for instance. Yet climatic conditions were such that the number of missionaries was depleted by death and disease. First Grant had died three weeks after landing, then Brunsden, then Fountain, who had been the first to join Carey and Thomas. Now, within three years, four more missionaries had died, among them John Thomas. Although he had not joined the missionaries at Serampore, he had served as a missionary of the Society in different places until his health deteriorated and he had to give up.

These latest deaths left only Carey, Marshman and Ward of those first seven missionaries sent out by the Baptist Missionary Society. These three became known as the Serampore Triad or Trio. They were, of course, supported by Carey's eldest sons, Felix and William, and the wives of Marshman and Ward and the few new missionaries who had recently arrived. But more were needed at a time when the work was increasing and doors of opportunity were opening.

Carey had the joy of seeing one after another of his sons

join the church. Felix had, from the age of fifteen, helped Ward in the mission press. He became a printer of oriental languages, a medical missionary and a very good linguist. He was later sent to Burma to assist in laying the foundations of a mission in that territory. While there he translated several portions of the Bible into the language of the country. Carey set a high standard for his sons, as he did for all Christians, and it was a great disappointment to him when this son, who had shown so much promise, left the mission to become Burmese ambassador to the Governor-General. He had performed a very useful service in Burma and gained many honours, but life for him was far from happy. He had the terrible experience of seeing his wife and children drown. This left him desolate. His mission as Burmese Ambassador did not succeed and for three years he stayed away from Serampore and the mission. Then, through an apparently chance meeting with William Ward, he came back to the mission.

William, Carey's second son, was married and ordained when he was twenty. He went to join Fernandez, the Portuguese convert in the Dinajpur area, where Carey had purchased his indigo factory before he went to Serampore. The place where William lived was very lonely, with only a few Europeans anywhere near. Wild buffaloes and dacoits (Indian robbers) frequented that area. These caused him so much alarm that he wrote to his father asking to be moved somewhere less dangerous. Carey himself, had endured similar dangers in the early days of his mission and he expected the same fearlessness from his sons. He wrote in reply:

'There is much guilt in your fears, dear William. Mary and you will be a thousand times safer committing yourselves to God in the path of duty than neglecting duty to take care of yourselves.'

Later, however, William was moved to Katwa, a much less lonely place, to the north of Calcutta.

Jabez, the son born while Carey was in the Isle of Wight awaiting a passage to India, came to Christ later than his elder brothers and did not, at once, join the mission staff. He studied law in Calcutta and became clerk to a Calcutta attorney. A year later, however, he was baptised, married and ordained. He then gave up excellent prospects in his profession and went to Amboyna, with Malay Bibles. He became a Christian missionary and State Superintendent of schools in an area with a population of fifty thousand natives. Five years later he responded to an urgent request for missionaries to be sent to Rajputana, in the Chittagongs, a four-month journey from Serampore, where he remained for fifteen years.

Jonathan, born in India, became a Supreme Court Attorney, but he showed interest in his father's work by looking after the finances of the mission in India.

Thus Carey's four sons took a lively part in the mission which meant so much to their father.

Their mother's health continued to be a source of anxiety. She died in December 1807, and the burden which Carey had borne for so long was lifted.

One of the greatest causes of grief and disappointment which came to the missionaries was the failure of some of their native Christians to maintain the standards required of them; in some cases even to keep their Christian faith. This was not entirely unexpected, for they were up against tremendous opposition because they had broken caste. The new way of life was so different from the past. Lying and stealing had then been an everyday occurrence.

Ward said at this time:

'How discouraged we sometimes are by their accusations, quarrels and apparent untruths; truly a missionary's hardest work is not travel in a hot climate.'

With great understanding Carey wrote:

> Compared with Europeans they are a larger sort of children. We are obliged to encourage, strengthen, counteract, disapprove, advise, teach and yet all so as to retain their warm affection. We have much to exercise our patience from the uncultivated state of their minds; but also, much to rejoice us in respect to their conduct and their acquisition of evangelical knowledge. Even when viewed at their worst, we can truly call them the excellent of Bengal.

All except one of these converts, demonstrated their repentance and came back into the fellowship to the great joy of the devoted Serampore Trio.

There were other causes for rejoicing. Carey's main missionary methods were preaching, teaching and translating the Bible. The Marshmans had, from the beginning, developed boys' and girls schools for European residents' children. These had been a source of much needed income for the mission. Now, in Serampore and every new station which was formed, Marshman opened a free school for the native population. These schools were often financed by Europeans living in India. The very young as well as older children attended. Those in the first class were converts under instruction. They were taught in Bengali the basic principles of Christianity. The second class learned to read and write in Bengali and in English, while the third class comprised children who had not lost caste and they were only taught Bengali.

The Serampore Trio, Carey, Marshman and Ward, worked together amazingly well, each being a support to the other, yet having their individual responsibilities. But it was to Carey, the one-time cobbler from a small Northamptonshire village, to whom they all looked as leader. He had the administration, the planning and the organising of this ever expanding work for God; he who had started it all under God. Now, at last, after more than seven years in India, the Bengal Christian church, though limited at present, was established.

This was the position at the end of the first year of the nineteenth century. The year 1801 was to bring added duties, with unexpected honour for Carey.

12

College Professor

THE EAST INDIA COMPANY'S CONTINUED REFUSAL TO allow missionaries to work in Calcutta was very frustrating for Carey and his colleagues. Here was a densely populated city where the native population was without any Christian teacher or preacher. Yet Carey and his fellow missionaries, who had come out to India expressly to spread the knowledge of God's love, were unable to reach out, though they were less than twenty miles away. But however successful the authorities in Calcutta might be in keeping the English missionaries shut away in Danish territory, they could not prevent the native converts from carrying the message to their own people, nor could they prevent the distribution of pages of the Bible which had been translated and printed by the missionaries.

But Carey longed for absolute freedom to preach the Gospel where and how he would. He was a man of vision and now that the work was established in one area, his thoughts and desires extended to other needy places.

Then, quite unexpectedly, the way opened. He had been settled in Serampore for about eighteen months when he received a letter from the Rev. David Brown, an Anglican minister who was chaplain to the white people in Calcutta. To Carey's amazement the letter offered him an appointment as Professor of Bengali in the British Governor General's new college at Fort William, in Calcutta. He was asked to cross the river to Barrackpore to discuss the offer.

As William Cowper wrote in the first verse, of his hymn:

> 'God moves in a mysterious way,
> His wonders to perform.'

In great excitement Carey laid the letter before his two colleagues, Marshman and Ward. They knew that Lord Wellesley, the Governor-General, had founded the college at Fort William with the intention of training young Englishmen who had come to India straight from public schools. Until now they had not bothered to learn Bengali or any other Indian language, and although they had little to do but the simplest clerical tasks, they did not attempt to acquire any knowledge of India's history or laws. Consequently, as more senior positions became available, they were promoted to work they were not qualified to do. Lord Wellesley was determined to alter all that. In future they were to be given a two-year course at the College and must pass an examination before they could qualify for positions of authority.

Carey's colleagues advised him to accept the post provided it did not interfere with his missionary labours. While Carey was enthusiastic about the opportunities this would give him, he was concerned about his qualifications. He had never aspired to being a professor. When, as a boy with a very limited education, he was studying Latin and

Greek, he little thought that he would one day be offered such a position.

On one thing he was determined. He would not even consider the proposition if it was likely to interfere with his work as a missionary.

He expressed these feelings later when he met the Rev. David Brown and Claudius Buchanan, who had been appointed Provost and Vice-Provost of the College. On the contrary, they told him, it would further the interests of the mission. He would be able to introduce the Bengali New Testament which he had translated and this would spread the message to other parts of the country. These two men were almost as anxious as Carey that a way should be open to preach to the Hindu in Calcutta and the district around. When they put Carey's application before the Governor-General they assured him that although there was no man more suited for the position, he would only accept it if he had absolute freedom to preach the Gospel. Lord Wellesley agreed!

Carey's only remaining doubt was that the task might prove too great for his abilities. Yet the man who had told others to attempt great things for God and expect great things from him, would never hold back from the opportunities of fulfilling the mission to which God had called him.

One small problem arose. Because he was not of the Anglican persuasion he would not be allowed, by the constitution of the college, to hold a professorship. Consequently he was engaged as a tutor, which carried the lower salary of five hundred rupees a month, or between six and seven hundred pounds a year. For Carey this was wealth indeed and would increase the funds of the mission considerably, enabling the missionaries to be self-supporting once more. Later, however, he was promoted to Professor, with a salary of one thousand rupees.

Although he would now be earning much more than ever before, it never occurred to him to keep the money for his own use. He sent some to help support his father and his invalid sister in England, but he paid the rest into the mission funds.

Any proof which he needed to confirm the rightness of his decision came only four days after he started at the college. Because of the long delays in communications at that time, it was not generally known that England was at war with Denmark. Consequently, when English troops took over the Government seat at Barrackpore, and ran up the Union Jack instead of the Danish flag, it came as a complete surprise. Had Carey not been in the strong position of a college teacher of languages at Calcutta, the mission press in Serampore might have had to be given up and the work of printing the Bible been halted. During the next year peace was proclaimed and Serampore was again controlled by the Danes.

In one of his letters Carey wrote:

'Few people know what may be done till they try and persevere in what they undertake.'

Had he not believed this he might not have dared to accept the position at Fort William and he would have shrunk from the task of translating the Bible into the many languages of the people of India.

Constantly he had to learn new languages, writing by hand, for there were no typewriters. Having learned the language and written the translation, there were all the problems of printing.

At first native paper was used. This proved unsatisfactory because bookworms and white ants devoured it. They liked the rice paste with which the paper was stiffened! During the printing process they attacked the sheets as they came off the press. Deliveries from England were costly and uncertain, and the only alternative was for the mission press to make its own paper. Various experiments were tried before it was decided to obtain a steam engine from England. This caused considerable interest among the natives, for it was the first to be seen in India. Crowds came from long distances to see this 'machine of fire', as they called it.

The paper so produced had its own trade mark — *Serampore* — and this was so satisfactory that it came to be the source of native paper.

Another problem was the provision of punches and types for the different languages, some of which had never previously been printed. Sir Charles Wilkins had made a name for himself in this connection, becoming known as the 'Caxton of India'. Once more the missionaries had evidence of help coming unexpectedly in time of need. It came this time in the form of Punchaman, a native blacksmith who had been taught the art of punch cutting and casting of types by Sir Charles Wilkins himself. Punchaman came to the Mission to ask for work just at the right time.

The amount of labour involved in translation of books other than the Bible is revealed in a letter which Carey sent to Ryland:

'I am now printing a dictionary of the Bengali,' he writes, 'which will be pretty large, for I have got to page 256, quarto, and am not near through the first letter. That letter, however, begins more words than any two others.'

Having learned Sanskrit and realised that this gave the key to the translation of most of the different languages of India, he wrote to the Missionary Society in England:

'We have it in our power, if our means would do for it, in the space of about fifteen years to have the Word of God translated and printed in all the languages of the East . . . On this great work we have fixed our eyes. Whether God will enable us to accomplish it or any part of it is uncertain.'

This proved to be over optimistic, but the founding of the British and Foreign Bible Society about that time gave them further funds to add to those sent by the Baptist churches in response to the call. It also provided further impetus, for Carey, Marshman and Ward were invited to join George Udney and the two chaplains – Brown and Buchanan – in forming an auxiliary of the Society in Bengal, and to serve on the local committee. For this they were to receive three hundred rupees a month to assist their translation work.

Once more Carey was proving, as he did all through his life, that, in one way or another, God supplies the need of the moment to those who have the faith to trust him.

With the assistance of his few colleagues and pundits Carey translated or edited and saw through the press thirty-six different translations of portions of the Bible. Through their distribution the Gospel was widely spread in and beyond Bengal.

With his characteristic energy and ability to adapt himself, in spite of his awareness of his lack of college training, Carey settled down to the position at Fort William which he was to hold with distinction for thirty years. For the whole of that period he divided his time between Calcutta and Serampore. At the beginning of the week he travelled by rowing boat down the winding Hooghli to Calcutta. He stayed in rooms at the College until Friday, when he made the eighteen mile river journey back to Serampore and continued his work there.

How he enjoyed his duties at the College. It gave him marvellous opportunities of extending his interest in languages and speeded up the translations of the Bible. Also he was in constant and close contact with the young men who were likely to hold high positions in the government of India in the future, and many of them became fine Christians.

These duties alone would have been sufficiently arduous for most men, but Carey was an evangelist as well as a translator. He could not forget the half-million natives who needed to hear the Gospel, and he the only resident missionary. Brown and Buchanan shared that interest. Though they were chaplains to the white community, they encouraged Carey to provide for the Indian population. This was the opportunity for which he had been waiting. He started meetings in private houses and within two years of his appointment had opened a place of worship in Calcutta, where he preached on two evenings a week in Bengali and in English, and took his turn with other missionaries in preaching twice on Sundays.

This was only a beginning. It was not long before he was drawing the other mission staff in to help. Krishna Pal was the first native missionary. By 1810 he was preaching at fourteen different places every week, including prisons and a factory, as well as visiting over forty families. Carey himself had no time for visiting, but he kept one evening a week free for visits from inquirers. About twenty came each week to discuss their problems with him.

Meanwhile his work at the college increased. He had been offered the position of teacher of Bengali because he was the only man in India entirely qualified to fill this post. Towards the end of his first term Carey was appointed also to teach Sanskrit. He had found it necessary to learn this ancient language in order to acquire a speedy knowledge of many other eastern languages. He explained, in the preface to his Sanskrit grammar, how a knowledge of this helped in learning other languages. He wrote:

> The peculiar grammar of any one of these [principal languages of India] may be acquired in a couple of months, and then the language lies open to the student. The knowledge of four words in five enables him to read with pleasure, and renders the acquisition of the few new words, as well as the idiomatic expressions, a matter of delight rather than of labour.

Not a single prose work was known to exist in the Bengali language when Carey became a professor, and he had to create his own textbooks. One of his earliest tasks was to arrange for the production of a Bengali and a Sanskrit grammar. In this he had the assistance of Ram Ram Basu, who had been his own earliest teacher. Altogether six grammars were produced and three dictionaries compiled under Carey's direction. As a member of the Asiatic Society, he was one of a wide circle of Europeans who were interested in Eastern literature, while at the college he had the advantage of meeting and talking with some of the most learned pundits (philosophers and teachers) of India.

At the end of the first three-year course in Sanskrit, a college 'Disputation' was held in the throne room of Government House. It was attended by the Governor-General, his brother, who later became the Duke of Wellington, all the principal officers of State; by judges; by commercial, civil and military people of prominence; by the Supreme Council, and the Council of the College. Pundits and Brahmins were also there; in fact, the assembly included all the wealth and learning of Bengal.

Carey was to be the principal speaker and his speech was to be delivered in Sanskrit.

Standing beside his three most proficient students, on the dais in the throne room, he listened as they addressed this august assembly in the language each had studied under his guidance. They were proud to stand beside their slightly bent, forty-three-year-old professor, his bald head surrounded by a little white hair.

With feelings of humility and gratitude to God who had led him to this day, Carey, Professor of Sanskrit and Bengali, addressed the Governor and the principal men in Bengal, in Sanskrit. It was a special honour for any of India's learned men, but peculiarly so for this particular Englishman who had worked and prayed for India, against considerable odds, for eleven years. His was the first Sanskrit speech made by a European. It was made by a man who had been refused admittance to Bengal when he arrived in 1793.

In his speech he declared himself a missionary. Six years earlier, when he was registered as an indigo planter, he could not admit to being a missionary if he wished to continue his work. Then he had written to Fuller saying that if ever he had the opportunity publicly to declare himself a missionary, he would do so.

He now redeemed that pledge.

Lord Wellesley commented:

'I am much pleased with Mr. Carey's truly original and excellent speech. I esteem such a testimony from such a man a greater honour than the applause of Courts and Parliaments.'

13

Fire

While Carey's duties at the college kept him in Calcutta during the week, William Ward worked steadily in the printing office at Serampore. There was always plenty to do and he often stayed on after the type founders, compositors, binders and other work-people had gone home.

On the evening of March 11th, 1812, Ward had stayed to settle some accounts. The work of translation was going ahead fast. A thousand reams of paper had been received only the previous week to fill an order from the Calcutta Bible Auxiliary, and he had a variety of types in different languages. With this order and the manuscripts of dictionaries, grammars and Bible translations, the presses would be kept busy for some time to come.

The light was fading when the missionary suddenly became aware that the room was filling with thick, choking smoke. He shouted to Marshman and rushed towards the type room from which the smoke was coming. Before he could discover the seat of the fire the density of the smoke sent him back. With doors and windows shut to prevent the spread of the fire, Ward climbed to the roof, made an opening, and kept a flow of water pouring on to the fire.

Marshman organised the natives, who started carrying outside whatever could be salvaged. When it seemed as though the water was beginning to bring the fire under control, someone opened a window! Immediately flames leapt up to the roof and the whole building was soon a mass of fire. The only hope now was to speed the salvage and let the fire burn itself out. Fortunately the presses were in the main room which had not caught fire. Some papers were saved but the precious grammars, Bible translations and other works could not be reached.

Much of the loss seemed irreparable and Marshman and Ward must have wondered how they were going to break the news to Carey. Work which had taken him years of patient toil had gone up in flames.

By midnight the whole length of the roof had fallen in and the fire was still continuing its work of destruction. It did not die down until two o'clock in the morning.

Masses of charred paper and molten metal lay all around as Marshman took a boat down the river to Calcutta that morning. As soon as Carey saw Marshman he knew that something was really wrong, but he was stunned when Marshman gently explained what had happened. The full extent of the damage was not known at that time, though they knew the grammar and Bible translation which were going through the press must have been destroyed. Marshman could happily report that there was no loss of life, and that the five presses had been removed in time to prevent their being damaged.

The ruins were still smoking when Carey and Marshman arrived at Serampore that day. The printing office itself was entirely burnt out with everything in it. The loss in paper alone was immense.

Ward had been busy clearing up in Marshman's absence. Trying to make the best of the matter he told them that he had recovered four thousand punches and the types of fourteen Indian tongues, the result of more than ten years' labour. He had already made arrangements to move into a warehouse near the river and use that as a printing office. With his usual cheerfulness Ward pointed out that though it was not as inviting as the building they had previously occupied, it was bigger, and would allow for growth. With the punches and types, the molten lead and other materials he had been able to salvage he anticipated they would be able to start printing again within a month.

That certainly was something to be thankful for, but Carey's losses were very serious.

Thomason, a chaplain friend of Carey's, described what he saw that day:

> The scene was indeed affecting. The immense printing office, two hundred feet long and fifty broad, reduced to a mere shell. The yard covered with burnt quires of paper, the loss in which article was immense. Carey walked with me over the smoking ruins. The tears stood in his eyes.
>
> 'In one short evening,' said he, 'the labours of years are consumed. How unsearchable are the ways of God! I had lately brought some things to the utmost perfection of which they seemed capable, and contemplated the missionary establishment with perhaps too much self-congratulation. The Lord has laid me low, that I may look more simply to him.'
>
> Who could stand in such a place, at such a time, with

such a man, without feelings of sharp regret and solemn exercise of mind. I saw the ground strewed with half-consumed paper, on which, in the course of a very few months, the words of life would have been printed. The metal under our feet amidst the ruins was melted into misshapen lumps — the sad remains of beautiful types consecrated to the service of the sanctuary. All was smiling and promising a few hours before — now all is vanished into smoke or converted into rubbish ...

A fortnight later Carey was able to write to Dr. Ryland:

The loss is very great and will long be severely felt; yet I can think of a hundred circumstances which would have made it much more difficult to bear. The Lord has smitten us, he had a right to do so, and we deserve his corrections. I wish to submit to his sovereign will, nay, cordially to acquiesce therein, and to examine myself rigidly to see what in me has contributed to this evil.

I now, however, turn to the bright side; and here I might mention what still remains to us ... Our loss, so far as I can see, is reparable in a much shorter time than I should at first have supposed ...

Still later he was able to write:

'We found, on making the trial, that the advantages in going over the same ground a second time, were so great that they fully counter-balanced the time requisite to be devoted thereto in a second translation.'

Such was the humility and the fighting spirit of the missionary band at Serampore, who allowed nothing to prevent them in the continuance of their work for God, and who saw advantages in adversity. Their faith and industry were rewarded, for the disastrous fire brought their work to the notice of people in Europe and America as well as in India. The financial loss was well over ten thousand pounds. Much of this was raised in England and Scotland alone in fifty days, while generous contributions came from friends in America, and from Thomason's congregation in India. Calcutta newspapers carried leading articles, one of which stated that the Serampore press 'like the phoenix of antiquity, would rise from its ashes, winged with new strength and destined, in a lofty and long-enduring flight, widely to diffuse the benefits of knowledge throughout the East'.

How different was the story now compared with the time when Carey had not been allowed to work in Calcutta.

14

Serampore College

GRADUALLY, OVER THE YEARS, THE BIBLE WAS BEING PUT into the hands of India's people. In 1801 the missionaries had rejoiced when they were able to place on the Communion table the first bound copy of the Bengali New Testament. Two thousand copies of this had been printed. Only eight years later Carey finished the Bengali translation of the whole Bible. When asked how much more of such work he planned, he replied:

'The work I have allotted to myself in translation will take me about twenty years.'

He was then forty-eight years of age.

That night he was sick and feverish. A couple of weeks later he became so ill that he was not expected to live. Toughened by his hard working life and his determination to plod on until he had finished the task to which he had set his hand, he recovered, and a month later was busy at his desk again.

He was greatly strengthened by his marriage to Lady Rumohr, which had taken place the previous year. Charlotte Rumohr was a Danish lady who had settled in Serampore a short distance from the mission, close to the paper mill. She was admirably suited to be Carey's wife and the thirteen years of their marriage were the happiest in his life. She did not have very good health but was intensely interested in Carey's work and, when she married, made over her house to the mission.

The mission premises had already been extended by the purchase of the adjoining house and grounds. This had enabled the school to be enlarged and had also provided more suitable premises for the growing printing and binding works, though much of this was destroyed in the fire.

Only the high caste Brahmins were the recognised Indian teachers and educationists at this time. Now Carey proposed to make Serampore a centre of Christian learning. One of his principles was that India could only be won by her own people. He planned to have a college where Indians of every class could acquire a knowledge of philosophy, religion, literature and science and attain such a high academic standard that they would be fully capable of teaching and leading their own people. It would be the first college to provide for the poorer Indian classes to receive higher education. He planned, among other things, to have a library, a teacher-training college and a theological institute with a four year course of approved training for future Indian ministers and missionaries.

The hope of such a centre of learning had been in Carey's mind for many years. Doubtless his certainty of its value became apparent as the European students who came under this teaching and influence at Fort William gained high positions as administrators in different parts of India and, in many cases, became a power for good. Why should not Indians equally be trained and exert Christian influence among their own people?

A prospectus, written by Dr. Marshman, was issued on July 15th, 1818, proposing:

'A College for the Instruction of Asiatic Christian and other youth in Eastern literature and European science.'

The idea had the full approval of the British Governor in India, Lord Hastings. He became the first patron, while the Danish Governor-General accepted the position of first Governor of the college.

A spacious and imposing building was erected on the riverside and opened in 1821. The cost of the building was fifteen thousand pounds and this was entirely borne by the Serampore Trio from their own earnings and from their private appeals. Contributions for equipment and other expenses were made by people in India, Britain and America.

In the first year thirty-seven students were enrolled; nineteen of whom were Christians, fourteen Hindus and four were 'without caste or religion'.

King Frederik VI of Denmark showed his appreciation of the work of these devoted missionaries by writing them a personal letter and presenting them each with a medal. That the modest Carey, so self-effacing, valued the letter, is shown by his writing on the lining of the case in which the medal was enclosed:

'It is my desire that this medal, and the letter of the King of Denmark, which accompanied it, be given at my death to my dear son Jonathan, that he may keep it for my sake.'

Six years later, when Marshman went to Denmark and had an audience with the king, a royal charter was drawn up, richly bound and embossed on vellum. It was read at the Court in Fredericksnagore in June 1827 and gave the power for the College to confer degrees on its qualified students. It gave the right of development along independent lines as a Christian university. Carey, Marshman and his son John were named as being elected and appointed as the Council of the College.

In the Statutes are the words:

'No caste, colour or country shall bar any man from admission to Serampore College.'

15

Sorrows and Solaces

IT WAS INEVITABLE THAT THE SMALL COMMITTEE WHO had formed the Society in Kettering should be depleted by death.

One of the most deeply felt by Carey was that of Andrew Fuller in 1815. During the twenty-two years since the foundation of the mission in Kettering, he had been its hard-working, capable and warm-hearted Secretary. He had made countless journeys throughout England and Scotland to speak about the mission and to collect subscriptions. It was by his organisation and effort that the money was so quickly raised to cover the loss sustained by the fire in the printing office. Carey was in constant correspondence with him and said:

'There was scarcely any other man in England to whom I could so completely lay open my heart.'

Following Fuller's death there arose a period of misunderstanding between the committee at home and the Serampore Triad, which caused much grief to Carey and his colleagues. New young missionaries were sent out who had different ideas from the older men who knew India and her peoples so well. It was hardly surprising that it took time to sort out problems and difficulties, especially with the Home Committee so far away and many of the members having no personal knowledge of the pioneers. On the other hand Carey and his colleagues resented having the financial position of the mission questioned when they had been supporting it with their own earnings.

All this caused the Serampore Triad great sorrow and had they not been so entirely devoted to their work it might have resulted in complete disruption. As it was they bore the complaints with patience and went on working for the time when complete understanding should exist once more, as indeed it did, though not until Ward and Marshman had each taken furloughs in England.

In a country so prone to disease and sharp climatic changes death could attack suddenly. Krishna Pal, who had been their first native convert, had been very effective as a pioneer missionary among people in many parts of India. In 1822, when he was only fifty years of age, he had the dreaded cholera which was responsible for the death of so many in India. Asked just before he died if he still loved Christ, he said:

'Yes, but not as much as he loves me.'

Later that year Felix, Carey's eldest son, died after a bout of fever. Since he had returned to Serampore he had been of enormous assistance to his father and was known as 'the completest Bengali linguist amongst India's Europeans'. Carey had mourned the death of his wife the previous year and now there was this further gap in the family.

But this was not the end of the sad story. In March of the following year Ward suffered a severe attack of cholera and died within a couple of days. He had only recently returned from a four-year furlough, when he had raised quite a large sum of money for the mission, and had come back full of vigour. He had won each of Carey's boys for Christ and had already begun winning students at the newly established college. He understood the Indian mind as few others did. Carey had singled him out in England as a possible future missionary and a close bond existed between the two from the time of their first meeting at Mudnabati.

With all that was engaging Carey's attention one would hardly have expected him to have time or mental and physical energy to devote to planting and cultivating a garden. Yet his interest in this never flagged but rather increased with advancing years.

Reference has already been made to the avenue of mahogany trees which he planted in the grounds at Serampore. The additional property acquired through the years at Serampore gave him a bigger acreage of ground on which to work — five acres in all. This provided him with the opportunity he had always desired, to create and develop a really good botanical garden.

When he first went to Bengal practically nothing was known about India's plants and animals. As he had done since he was a child living in Paulerspury, Carey studied these and made meticulous notes, keeping separate notebooks for different species. There were many new ones to be observed. The white ants were very destructive, destroying everything on which they fastened. They had even been known to eat through an oak chest in a matter of days and then to devour its contents. Butterflies were not as numerous as in England, and they were different. There were many birds, such as pigeons and sparrows similar to those he had known in Whittlebury Woods. There were water wagtails, ducks and geese, grasshoppers and crickets.

When writing to friends in England Carey asked them to send him packets of seeds or plants which could be introduced in Bengal. The commonest of English wild flowers, such as the daisy, were planted with loving care. Equally, when writing to his missionary friends and colleagues in different areas in the East, he asked for specimens of plants which did not grow in Bengal.

With the help of friends, seedsmen and agriculturalists, he had gradually developed the Serampore Botanical Garden. It contained one of the finest botanical collections in Asia and became as widely known as that belonging to the East India Company in Calcutta, to which he had applied for a position as an Assistant in his early days in India when he was homeless. Dr. Roxburgh, the superintendent of the garden, became a personal friend, and they constantly exchanged specimens and advice.

Carey loved to walk in his garden in the early morning, and again at the close of the day's toil. He, perhaps more than many, needed such a place. Here he could relax from the strain of living such a full life. He made it a place of prayer and meditation. He had created it as much for the glory of God as any other part of his work.

Yet even this peaceful garden, created and tended with such loving care, was to be made a scene of desolation.

About six months after Ward's death the Damoodar river overflowed its banks and swept through the country as far as the Hooghli. Very many people, as well as cattle, were drowned, and numberless houses were destroyed. The missionary grounds and Carey's garden lay under three feet of water. When the water subsided it was a sorry spectacle that came to view. Precious plants had either been swept away or were buried under a layer of sand.

Carey was confined to bed when this happened. He was suffering from a fever so severe that once more his life was in danger. The fever was the result of a dislocated hip-joint sustained when he slipped on stepping from his boat. As the water swept along its treacherous path it reached Carey's house and he had to be carried out before the house, too, was destroyed.

Once more he made a good recovery, though he was lame and had to walk with a stick. Yet he put his garden in order and sent home for more seeds to replace his losses. Later, a cyclone caused even more damage, but again he made it good. Nothing seemed to daunt him. When and where there was destruction he would build again.

It was not only for his own pleasure that he had developed his garden. He wanted to use it to show the people of India what could be done to improve the agricultural position of the country. Under his instigation an Agri-Horticultural Society was founded in 1820, with the Governor-General as patron. Within a few weeks fifty people had been enrolled as members.

The Society aimed to give practical scientific advice to its members of whatever class, on how to make the best use of the land at their disposal. Carey performed many services for agriculture and was invited to serve on the committee dealing with the preservation of the timber supply of Bengal.

In 1823 he was elected President of the Agricultural Society he had formed. He was also elected a Fellow of the Linnaean Society of London (which was concerned with a particular classification of plants) a member of the Geological Society, and he became a corresponding member of the Royal Horticultural Society.

These were the honours which came to the man who, as a boy, worked in his father's garden and later created his own small gardens in obscure villages in Northampton. He did not seek honours or rewards. All he did arose out of his love for God and his fellow men.

16

Carey's Death

AMONG THOSE WHO HAD CROWDED INTO WIKOW WALLIS'S parlour when the Baptist Missionary Society was founded was William Staughton, a theological student from Bristol College. His particular friends were John Sutcliff and Andrew Fuller and it was probably they who invited him to be present. He must have been interested in Missions for he contributed his half guinea ($52\frac{1}{2}$p). Later he accepted a pastorate in America, and corresponded regularly with Fuller and with Carey. It was largely through Staughton's exertions that America showed an interest in the Baptist Missionary Society from its earliest days, and that the American Baptist Missionary Convention was formed, with Staughton dealing with secretarial duties similarly to those which Fuller performed in England. From the time he met Carey in Widow Wallis's parlour he was an advocate of foreign missions.

Besides giving monetary support to Carey and his colleagues, America sent her own missionaries to India. The enthusiasm of a group of American Congregational students was later responsible for the institution of the American Board of Foreign Missions. Among this group were

Adoniram and Ann Judson, who, on their way to Serampore, had become Baptists by conviction. Like the British missionaries before them, they were not welcomed by the East India Company, and eventually went to Burma to join Felix Carey until the American Baptist Missionary Society was formed. Eventually they took over the work there on behalf of the American Baptist Missionary Society. Thus Britain and America had close links in their missionary activities at that time. This was further shown when, in 1807, Brown University awarded Carey the diploma of Doctor of Divinity. This was done at a time when British universities would not grant degrees to any who were not members of the established church.

Carey, like Fuller in England, seldom took a break. Yet, despite this, and his many attacks of fever, he remained active almost to the end of his days, though for the last few years he became visibly weaker.

Each of his four sons had children and Carey enjoyed having them around. In one letter he writes:

'Eliza was shy at first but is now very friendly. The first word Felix said to me was "Papa". He is friendly with everyone and he and Eliza are as happy as can be wished. Margaret is a complete romp.'

It is not surprising that children liked him, for he had many childlike qualities, particularly humility. His whole life exemplified Christ's words when he set a child in the midst of his disciples and said:

'Whosoever shall humble himself as this little child, the same is greatest in the kingdom of heaven.'

Having left England in 1793, Carey never returned, but made India, and Bengal in particular, his country. Its needs were his care. His concern at the number of poor people who borrowed money from money lenders at extortionate rates of interest, led him to take an interest in the system of savings banks which the Goverment were encouraging. But his greatest contribution to the people of India was the gift of the Bible translated into their own language. Dr. Marshman said of him after his death:

'Carey has scarcely left a translation to be attempted on this side of India.'

Yet from the day of his appointment in 1793 to the day of his death, Carey did not receive more than six hundred pounds from the Society's funds. He earned his own living and contributed something like forty thousand pounds or more to Baptist missionary work in India.

During his final years he was not able to walk in his garden, but had a box put on wheels so that he might be pushed around in it.

One of his last visitors was that great missionary, Alexander Duff, who had landed in India in 1830. As he was leaving, Carey called him back and said:

'Mr. Duff, you have been speaking about Dr. Carey. When I am gone say nothing about Dr. Carey, speak about Dr. Carey's Saviour.'

William Carey died on June 9th, 1834, having said, shortly before his death, that he had 'no doubts, no fears and not a wish was left unsatisfied'.

He was buried in the mission burying ground. The road to the cemetery was lined with natives, as his body was borne to its last resting place. The Danish flag was flown at half mast and the Danish Governor and his wife and members of the council, as well as representatives from Calcutta attended the funeral.

'If I begin a thing I must finish it,' he said when a boy.

'Expect great things from God, Attempt great things for God,' he said as a young man.

As an older man at the end of his forty Indian years he could say:

'I have run the race that was set before me, I have finished the course. To God be the glory.'